C000023607

BBC Proms

The BBC presents the 116th seaso of Henry Wood Promenade Concerts broadcast live on BBC Radio 3

BBC RADIO 3

90–93FM

You can also enjoy regular Proms broadcasts on BBC Television throughout the summer, including on BBC HD in High Definition and 5.1 surround sound. And you can listen and watch again at your leisure for seven days after broadcast via the BBC iPlayer at bbc.co.uk/iplayer.

BBC One | BBC TWO | BBC three | BBC FOUR | BBC HD

BBC WORLD SERVICE | BBC RADIO 2 | BBC iPlayer

The Proms 1895–2010

The Proms was founded to bring the best of classical music to a wide audience in an informal setting. From the very outset, part of the audience has always stood in the 'promenade'. Prom places originally cost just a shilling (5p); today, standing places at the Royal Albert Hall cost only £5.00, and over 500 tickets go on sale for every concert there from one hour beforehand. Programmes have always mixed the great classics with what Henry Wood, the first conductor of the Proms, called his 'novelties' – in other words, rare works and premieres.

1895 The 26-year-old Henry Wood launches the Promenade Concerts at the newly opened Queen's Hall, Langham Place; Wood conducts the Proms throughout their first 50 years **1927** The BBC takes over the running of the Proms **1930** The new BBC Symphony Orchestra becomes the orchestra of the Proms **1939** Proms season abandoned after only three weeks following the declaration of war **1941** The Proms moves to the Royal Albert Hall after the Queen's Hall is gutted in an air raid **1942** The season is shared between two orchestras for the first time: the BBC Symphony Orchestra and the London Philharmonic **1947** First televised Last Night **1961** First complete opera heard at the Proms: Mozart's *Don Giovanni*, given by Glyndebourne Festival Opera **1966** First foreign orchestra at the Proms: the Moscow Radio Orchestra, under Gennady Rozhdestvensky **1970** First Late Night Prom: cult pop group The Soft Machine **1971** First 'world music' Prom: sitar-player Imrat Khan **1994** The Proms celebrates its 100th season with a retrospective of past premieres **1995** The Proms celebrates its centenary year with a season of new commissions **1996** First Proms Chamber Music series; first Prom in the Park **1998** First Blue Peter Family Prom signalling a new commitment to music for families **2002** The Proms goes digital on BBC Four; on-demand listening begins online **2003** Proms in the Park reaches out to all four nations of the UK with the unique festive atmosphere of the Last Night **2005** Proms Chamber Music moves to Cadogan Hall **2008** The Proms Plus series expands to precede every main evening Proms concert **2009** Over 1000 ukulele enthusiasts join the Ukulele Orchestra of Great Britain in a rendition of *Jerusalem*; the Proms Family Orchestra makes its Proms debut

The BBC: bringing the Proms to you – in concert, on radio, on television and online bbc.co.uk/proms

BBC Proms

CONCERT LISTINGS

BOOKING INFORMATION

VENUE INFORMATION

Printed using vegetable-based inks on FSC-certified paper. Established in 1993 as a response to concerns over global deforestation, FSC (Forest Stewardship Council) is an independent, non-governmental, not-for-profit organisation established to promote the responsible management of the world's forests. For more information, please visit www.fsc-uk.org.

Cover illustration: *Andy Potts.* **This page:** *Shutterstock; International Mahler Society, Vienna (spectacles); Lebrecht Music & Arts/Wolfgang Schweizer/Lightroom Photos/TopFoto/ArenaPAL (Scriabin); Chris Christodoulou/BBC (Wood); Simon Jay Price/BBC (Lewis); Chris Christodoulou/BBC (children's Prom); 20th Century Fox/Ronald Grant Archive ('Carousel'); Lebrecht Music & Arts ('The Sound of Music'); akg-images (Düsseldorf); ColouriserAL/Lebrecht Music & Arts (Bach)*

FSC
Mixed Sources
Product group from well-managed forests and other controlled sources
Cert no. SA-COC-1502
www.fsc.org
© 1996 Forest Stewardship Council

Welcome to the
BBC Proms 2010

The bust of Henry Wood, founder-conductor of the Proms, watches over us each season from the back of the Royal Albert Hall stage, and I like to think that he would be immensely proud of how the BBC has developed his vision of presenting the greatest classical music to the widest audience. What would he think of what's on offer at the BBC Proms in 2010?

Someone buying a Weekend Promming Pass for the opening weekend this season can hear Bryn Terfel in *The Mastersingers of Nuremberg* and Plácido Domingo in *Simon Boccanegra* – for just £12.50. Not only that, but they also get Mahler's Symphony No. 8 into the bargain. That celebratory opening weekend sets the festival spirit for the season – and the opera theme reaches a grand climax at the Last Night, as we urge the whole country to form the largest ever operatic chorus!

As ever, great orchestras, ensembles and soloists from around the world congregate at the Royal Albert Hall to perform a huge range of music over 58 days. Thanks to the BBC's continuing commitment, ticket prices are held at last year's levels, while Promming tickets still cost only £5.00;

The Henry Wood Day evening concert gives us a chance to revisit some of the pieces dedicated to or associated with Wood, and throughout the season we feature a number of works of which he gave the world or UK premieres. If you are interested in the history of Proms programming, you'll be pleased to know that later this year we will be making available the complete database of Proms performances since the festival began in 1895 – a real treasure-trove of information. Watch out for information about this, and everything else relating to the Proms, on the Proms website.

Building on the festival spirit, we devote a whole day to J. S. Bach – including the complete Brandenburg Concertos performed by Sir John Eliot Gardiner's English Baroque Soloists, an organ recital and an evening Prom celebrating grand orchestral arrangements. August Bank Holiday Monday marks another festive day, with a morning children's concert and an evening of popular classical and silver-screen favourites.

Our two Beethoven Nights revive a long-standing early Proms tradition, while Paul Lewis performs all five Beethoven piano concertos, joining a number of featured artists who make several visits during the season. These include conductors Sir Charles Mackerras, Sir Simon Rattle and Sir John Eliot Gardiner and violinist Julia Fischer. ▶

and the Proms reaches an even wider audience through broadcasts on BBC radio, television and online. The Proms Plus series of free daily pre-concert events offers audiences a rich context by introducing the background to the music (*see pages 88–91*), and our ever-broadening Proms Learning activities this year bring a new series of Music Intro events for adults, as well as a series of workshops for children in collaboration with the Royal College of Music. All of this – not forgetting the concerts themselves, which mix familiar repertoire with new musical journeys – proves that Henry Wood's vision lies firmly at the heart of the Proms today.

Festival days ... Beethoven Nights

It's truly apt, then, that we are honouring our founder-conductor in a special Henry Wood Day on Sunday 5 September (*see pages 62–65*). This begins with a FREE afternoon Prom, recreating the programme conducted by Wood at the Last Night of 1910 (slightly updated to include a new commission, reflecting Wood's tireless enthusiasm for what he called 'novelties'). This gargantuan concert not only gives us a flavour of programmes from Proms past, but means that we have, for the first time, two Last Nights of the Proms in one season!

CLOCKWISE FROM TOP LEFT: Broadway magic (Proms 19 & 49), Plácido Domingo (Prom 3), Proms founder-conductor Henry Wood; Family fun (*see pages 88–91*), Renée Fleming (Prom 76)

Glittering orchestras … composer anniversaries

Illustrious international visitors – from the USA, Australia and all corners of Europe – include the Berlin Philharmonic Orchestra with Rattle, the Czech Philharmonic Orchestra under Gardiner, the Minnesota Orchestra with Osmo Vänskä and the Sydney Symphony under Vladimir Ashkenazy.

It's also a delight to welcome back the World Orchestra for Peace (comprising hand-picked players from more than 70 international orchestras) under Valery Gergiev. Their Prom represents a notable instalment of our major Mahler anniversary celebrations this season – launched with the First Night's Symphony No. 8 ('Symphony of a Thousand'), 100 years after its world premiere and 80 years since Henry Wood introduced it to British audiences.

Maria João Pires, returning to the Proms after more than 10 years, marks the bicentenary of Chopin's birth in an intimate late-night piano recital, and our celebrations for Robert Schumann – also born in 1810 – include a cycle of his four symphonies. In addition, the season throws a spotlight on several non-anniversary composers, among them Scriabin and Parry, who deserves to be remembered for more than *Jerusalem*.

Unique events … new music

After its overwhelming success in 2008, we welcome back the Doctor Who Prom, complete with an appearance by the most recent Doctor, Matt Smith, while other unmissable events include: celebrations of Rodgers and Hammerstein (in the 50th anniversary of Hammerstein's death) and Stephen Sondheim (80 this year); and performances by jazz superstar Jamie Cullum and by the inimitable Penguin Cafe.

Henry Wood showed remarkable commitment to the music of his day. He would be delighted to see that we have 14 BBC commissions this year – many of them reflecting the current high point in the quality and range of British composers – alongside a wide spectrum of other living composers, such as Hans Abrahamsen, Brett Dean, Arvo Pärt (75 this year) and Bent Sørensen.

The BBC's own performing groups provide a vital continuity to the Proms. To plan so much new and unusual programming without them would be impossible, and we should never take them – or the quality of their performances – for granted. With 11 performances this season, the BBC Symphony Orchestra remains the resident ensemble – and has gone from strength to strength under its Chief Conductor Jiří Bělohlávek.

The Proms is a huge collaborative effort and I owe an enormous debt of thanks to my colleagues in the Proms team for their extraordinary work and professionalism.

We all wish you a very enjoyable summer at the BBC Proms.

Roger Wright

Roger Wright
Controller, BBC Radio 3 and Director, BBC Proms

P.S. This year we have devised a new booking system, which we hope you will find fairer and easier to use. All booking – whether online, in person or by phone – opens on Tuesday 4 May. For more details, see pages 150–151.

Valery Gergiev (Proms 26 & 41)   Nicola Benedetti (Prom 23)   Jamie Cullum (Prom 55)

EDINBURGH INTERNATIONAL FESTIVAL

'Following the light of the sun, we left the Old World.

Christopher Columbus

Adams's *El Niño* / The Gershwins'® *Porgy and Bess*ˢᴹ / Graun's *Montezuma* / Mahler's 3rd and 8th symphonies / Mozart's *Idomeneo* / Purcell's *The Indian Queen* / Puccini's *The Girl of the Golden West* / Ravel's *L'Heure espagnole* / BBC Symphony Orchestra / BBC Scottish Symphony Orchestra / The Cleveland Orchestra / Donald Runnicles / Finnish Radio Symphony Orchestra / Franz Welser-Möst / Gunther Schuller / Hélène Grimaud / Jonathan Biss / Joyce DiDonato / Kronos Quartet / Llŷr Williams / Magdalena Kožená / Mariss Jansons / Meredith Monk / Melvyn Tan / Midori / Mikhail Pletnev / Minnesota Orchestra / Nash Ensemble / Scottish National Jazz Orchestra / Opera Australia / Opéra de Lyon / Osmo Vänskä / Paco Peña / Royal Concertgebouw Orchestra / Royal Scottish National Orchestra / Russian National Orchestra / Sakari Oramo / Scottish Chamber Orchestra / Škampa Quartet / Sir Charles Mackerras / Simón Bolívar String Quartet / Steven Osborne / Susan Graham / Sydney Symphony Orchestra / The Sixteen / Trio Zimmermann / Vladimir Ashkenazy

Take a journey of discovery through Festival 2010

Call for your free brochure +44 (0)131 473 2000 or visit eif.co.uk

Supported by the City of Edinburgh Council and Scottish Arts Council. Charity No SC004694.

L'ORÉAL

Far from merely rolling up one's sleeves and reaching for a blank sheet of paper, putting together a Proms season involves an intricate balancing act. Helen Wallace talks to Proms Director Roger Wright about the challenges of planning the world's greatest classical music festival

B ack in the 1920s, planning the Proms proceeded at a gentle pace: 'We would spend the whole of the first day sharpening pencils and then go to Prada's for a bottle of Châteauneuf-du-Pape!' So claimed Henry Wood's concerts manager, W. W. Thompson, who came to the BBC with the Proms in 1927. Fast-forward to 2010, and current Director of the BBC Proms Roger Wright is more likely to be emailing a conductor about the 2013 season, or discussing a date in 2011, or commissioning a composer for a work in 2014, than watching the wine breathe. There's also the question of scale: while Wood first introduced a series of 49 concerts in the new Queen's Hall, Wright is now masterminding almost 90 concerts across two venues, all broadcast live, and 25 of them televised.

Planning the

'There's no blank sheet of paper,' says Wright – just a monumentally complicated puzzle that needs solving. First on the slate are the visiting orchestras, who are the most limiting in terms of relatively fixed touring schedules. 'We speak to these orchestras, their agents and our colleagues at the international festivals to see how their touring schedules and repertoire are going to fit in.' Next come the BBC groups, who are the resident ensembles of the Proms: 'Planning for the Proms is part of our ongoing conversations. We know which of the groups' commissions might be suitable for the Proms, what each of their conductors might take on.' The big opera performances involve so many artists, they also have to come early in the process, then significant composer anniversaries are noted (this year Schumann, Mahler, Arvo Pärt and George Benjamin, for example), though Wright is quick to point out that an anniversary in itself is never a reason to include a piece: 'it has to be worthwhile in its own right'. Then there are the rarities – which this year include three symphonies and the piano concerto by Scriabin. 'I asked Valery Gergiev if he would feature Scriabin's Symphony No. 1. He liked the idea, so was happy to do it; and I'm delighted that Vassily Sinaisky will conduct Parry's *Symphonic Fantasia* (Symphony No. 5) – we tend only to hear *Jerusalem*, and it's time we explored more. I would never force a piece on an artist, though. The last thing you want is a performer saying, "Look, I'll do it, if you really want me to."

Each programme must meet the criteria of an imaginary checklist, derived from the ideals of Henry Wood himself: 'I'm increasingly struck by the importance of heritage. This festival has developed over 115 years, and one holds the keys only for a short time, so retaining its unique identity is crucial. Part of the DNA of the Proms is a vital link

Well-known conductors exploring rarities this season: Valery Gergiev (left) and Vassily Sinaisky

between accessibility and quality. You could have the most distinctive music festival in the world, and no-one might turn up. The Proms has to be popular, so that you can achieve its other goal of taking the maximum number of people on a musical adventure.' But a balance has to be struck within the programmes, and within the budget, 'so that we include core repertoire, less familiar work and new music (what Wood called his "novelties"), as well as great artists and orchestras from all over the world.' Henry Wood might not have comprehended the red button service accessible via digital television or Proms twittering, but he would certainly still recognise his festival.

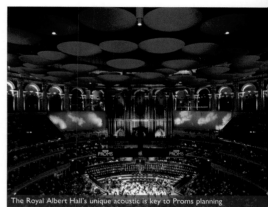

The Royal Albert Hall's unique acoustic is key to Proms planning

Another vital element is the Royal Albert Hall itself. If its acoustic suits the great symphonies of Bruckner, Mahler and Sibelius, it has its limitations too: 'Some pieces just don't work,' says Wright. 'There's something about the particular texture and pitch of Schumann's Cello Concerto which doesn't project in the Hall, but put a solo cellist playing a Bach suite on stage and you can hear every note.' The atmosphere of the Hall plays a role in programming too. There's a special sort of quiet that can be achieved by an audience of 5,000 people, but it doesn't necessarily happen the moment the lights go down – some crafty manipulation may be needed. Wright and conductor Edward Gardner discussed whether Britten's *Four Sea Interludes from 'Peter Grimes'* were the best way to start Prom 42 this year, with that fragile opening tune of 'Dawn' on high violins and flutes. They concluded a different work was needed to set the tone, and chose Arvo Pärt's mesmerising *Cantus in memoriam Benjamin Britten*.

Above all, Wright's aim is that each concert should be a singular event: 'The Proms has to be original, unexpected, creating juxtapositions that challenge the audience and illuminate the standard repertoire. Take Prom 35: we're really fortunate that in addition to the Danish National Symphony Orchestra, who are playing Sibelius's Fifth Symphony and Tchaikovsky's Violin Concerto, we could also draw on their Concert Choir and Vocal Ensemble – who will perform Ligeti's *a cappella* choruses *Night* and *Morning*, and in Ligeti's *Lux aeterna* and Langgaard's *Music of the Spheres* – before the ▶

Proms

Sarah Coleman (p10 illustration); Marco Borggreve/Decca (Gergiev); Chris Christodoulou/BBC (above right)

Handcrafted Perfection

Steinway & Sons pianos are individually created, which gives them their own unique characteristics and incomparable sound. Suffice to say that those at the top of their profession, as well as those who simply want the best, invest in nothing less.

"STEINWAY & SONS IS THE ONLY PIANO ON WHICH THE PIANIST CAN DO EVERYTHING HE WANTS, AND EVERYTHING HE DREAMS"

VLADIMIR ASHKENAZY

STEINWAY & SONS

STEINWAY HALL, 44 MARYLEBONE LANE, LONDON W1U 2DB   TEL: 020 7487 3391

orchestra ends with the Sibelius. The spaciousness of Langgaard's piece has a resonance with the Sibelius. The pay-off is that you fall into the arms of Sibelius – but with new ears.

Such a distinctive mix of music, new, familiar and new-to-the-Proms, is a key legacy of Henry Wood. 'It's important to remind ourselves what he did: he brought Mahler's Symphony No. 8 to this country, for example, in 1930 – his record of premieres is phenomenal.' Eighty years on, the season will open with this 'Symphony of a Thousand', and the Berlin

'I start to get concerned about a season until I stare at it and discover it has acquired a life of its own.'

Philharmonic brings Schoenberg's Five Orchestral Pieces, Op. 16, another Wood 'novelty'. In some respects Wright is returning to an earlier mode of planning in abandoning extramusical 'themes': 'I'm in the happy position of having seen themes successfully delivered by my predecessors, but I think we're in a period now where, by dint of the sheer number of concerts, it would be incredibly difficult to impose a theme, because the majority of concerts wouldn't relate to it. You end up trying to force in items to bolster the theme, rather than making the musical experience a priority.'

He has other strategies for creating a festival, focusing particularly on artists: 'Featured artists can be as important as featured composers. We had Stephen Hough doing all the Tchaikovsky concertos last year, and this year Paul Lewis will play all the Beethoven piano concertos with four different orchestras; Sir Simon Rattle conducts three concerts and Sir John Eliot Gardiner makes four appearances; Julia Fischer is playing a concerto as well as giving a Proms Chamber Music recital. I want the sense of welcoming back old friends.' Wright describes a moment in the creation of a season when it begins to direct him: 'I start to get concerned about a season

until I stare at it and discover it has acquired a life of its own; then ideas begin to evolve organically. We didn't initially set out to have a multiple piano strand last year, but we had discussed Stravinsky's ballets (of which *Les noces* requires four pianos); then we realised we already had a new two-piano concerto by Louis Andriessen, and decided to build on the idea by commissioning Anna Meredith to write a new piece for two pianos and ensemble.' Equally, this year, Monteverdi's *Vespers of 1610* suggests further Venetian reflections in a late-night Vivaldi Prom and a Venice-themed Proms Chamber Music concert.

The Late Night Proms have an atmosphere all of their own, as Wright explains: 'There has to be a real reason for the music to be performed at that time: the ideal late-night programme lasts under 90 minutes and has an intimate, informal feel.' If it's hard to pin down the 'Late Night' essence, there are plenty of good examples this year: Sir Charles Mackerras directs Mozart and Dvořák serenades, Jamie Cullum links up with the Heritage Orchestra, Ilan Volkov conducts the BBC Scottish Symphony Orchestra in Cage, Cardew, Feldman and Skempton, and the free-spirited Penguin Cafe makes an appearance.

The lunchtime Proms Chamber Music concerts at Cadogan Hall also play a distinctive role. Edward Blakeman, the Radio 3 Editor who programmes the series, is clear about its character: 'The programming is partly proactive, but mainly reactive to the main series. It's there to add insight and resonance, to be a distillation of the season. Often the chamber music series can throw a different light on a featured composer, or composer anniversary. For instance, it's wonderful to be doing Schumann's *Dichterliebe* with Mark Padmore and Imogen Cooper this season. One of the first concerts we did was a concert of Percy Grainger and Arvo Pärt with the

choir Polyphony. It was fairly outrageous but rather wonderful, and I've held on to that combination – we should always be pushing the envelope, trying to find that festival flavour, while asking, "What does the audience want to hear on a sunny Monday lunchtime?"

Another building block of the chamber music series is a new commission: this year, Radio 3 New Generation Artists Meta4 have chosen Jouni Kaipainen to write a new string quartet for them. Commissioning and premieres obviously play a major part in the Proms as a whole. The BBC Symphony Orchestra alone will give world premieres of works by Huw Watkins, Mark-Anthony Turnage and Tansy Davies, not to mention the London premieres of Colin Matthews's Violin Concerto and George Benjamin's *Duet* for piano and orchestra.

Chief Producer of the BBC Symphony Orchestra, Ann McKay explains the orchestra's unique role: 'Because we are playing up to 13 concerts per season, we dedicate our summer to the festival and can plan in the rehearsals for the big, technically complex new pieces, or those involving large forces and the chorus too. I'll be planning Proms rehearsals from April ▶

Many pianos make hard work: hiring, tuning and transporting – times four – were part of the logistical challenges behind last year's Multiple Pianos day at the Proms

onwards, and we have to allow time to discover each new piece. Early on I'll be in touch to discuss requirements with the composer, but there are always unknowns.' A composer's style might have changed in the two- or three-year period since they were commissioned; or, more commonly, they may not have written to length. One composer over-wrote by half an hour: 'I had to threaten that we would cut 10 minutes of his piece, but I seem to remember a combination of his cuts and the fact that it was conducted extremely fast brought us through on the night!'

And so to July, when the plans become reality. Scheduling rehearsals for a continuous festival of nearly 90 concerts running across 58 consecutive days, with up to four events happening

> Scheduling rehearsals is an administrative challenge. Little wonder that organ rehearsals have to take place between the hours of 2.00am and 4.00am.

on one day, is an administrative challenge of mind-boggling proportions. Not only does every concert need a rehearsal in the Hall, each one needs to be audio-balanced for live broadcasting, and often for televising too. Little wonder that organ rehearsals have to happen between the hours of 2.00am and 4.00am. When the concert itself is imminent, the 'to do' list stretches to pages: it covers piano and harp tuning, allowing time for the orchestra to settle on stage, the number of As to be given for tuning, and arranging towels and water for the conductor and soloist. Planning reaches a peak for the Last Night, when the event is not only televised live but links up with the Proms in the Park events. The meticulous work of the Proms team has been a revelation to Wright since he became Director: 'I'd seen the Proms close-up from Radio 3 for years, but now I'm inside it, I'm in awe of the Proms team, and the minute detail of the concert planning: they second-guess every eventuality, calculate everything minute by minute, and always want to do more.' ●

Helen Wallace is Consultant Editor of *BBC Music Magazine* and a former Editor of *The Strad*. She has written histories of the music publishers Boosey & Hawkes and of the Orchestra of the Age of Enlightenment, and is a regular critic on BBC Radio 4's *Front Row*.

Chris Christodoulou/BBC

GOING WITH THE FLOW
Unforeseeable situations from seasons past

Sir Thomas Allen at last year's Proms, 35 years after fainting on live television during a performance of Carl Orff's *Carmina burana* in 1974

 Leading the Proms dramas chart is the LSO's 1974 *Carmina burana*, in which baritone Thomas Alllen fainted from heat exhaustion on live TV. He was carted off after slumping forward into the cellos. André Previn continued conducting until a young man appeared on stage and said 'I can do it!'. 'For a moment,' Previn said, 'I thought, "Perhaps this guy's crazy!"' But then I thought, "What the hell?"' He turned out to be Patrick McCarthy, a young professional singer who acquitted himself with aplomb.

 Surely the most ill-fated work to be programmed was John Adams's *Short Ride in a Fast Machine*. It was first pulled from the Last Night in 1997, in the wake of Princess Diana's death in a car accident; it was then cancelled in 2001 after the air attacks on the World Trade Center. It finally received its Proms premiere in 2004, at the Blue Peter Prom.

 The entire programme for the Last Night was changed in just four days in response to the 9/11 attacks on New York in 2001. There were no flights from the USA, so Frederica von Stade had to pull out. Last Night party favourites – Elgar's *Pomp and Circumstance* March No. 1 and Wood's *Fantasia on British Sea-Songs* were pulled – as was Constant Lambert's jolly *Rio Grande*. The resulting event, conducted by American Leonard Slatkin, struck a more sombre note, with the finale from Beethoven's Ninth Symphony and Barber's Adagio for Strings.

 A stage manager had to kick down a dressing room door when the computer system crashed and swipe cards failed to operate the electronic locks. The Dresden Staatskapelle was tuned on stage and conductor Bernard Haitink waiting in the wings, but the principal viola, who was due to play a solo, couldn't reach his instrument.

 Gustavo Dudamel encountered a hurdle when at short notice he replaced Neeme Järvi (who had suffered a heart attack) for a Prom with the Gothenburg Symphony Orchestra. A high-pitched hum caused by feedback from the Hall's PA system could not be switched off and the concert was delayed by 45 minutes. In the end the whole system had to be disabled before Dudamel could lift his baton.

 New hand-baggage restrictions announced in August 2006, following attempts to detonate liquid explosives aboard aircraft leaving the UK, meant that New York's Orchestra of St Luke's could not carry on their instruments. They were forced to cancel their concerts at the Proms and the Edinburgh Festival, and the City of London Sinfonia stepped in.

 There must have been a jinx on Jiří Bělohlávek's first Prom as the BBC Symphony Orchestra's new Chief Conductor at the First Night of 2006. The conductor got stuck in a taxi in grid-locked traffic along Kensington High Street. In desperation he jumped out, leapt into a bicycle rickshaw and arrived just in time.

 A shoulder injury caused Maxim Vengerov to pull out of his Late Night Prom featuring Benjamin Yusupov's *Viola Tango Rock Concerto*, in which he would have played both acoustic and electric instruments and danced the tango. The piece had been written for him, so nobody could replace him. As an equally entertaining alternative – and retaining the concert's Latin-American feel – the brass ensemble of the Simón Bolívar Youth Orchestra of Venezuela swung into action, rushing down from Edinburgh to take the stage at 11.00pm. The crowds were still cheering after midnight …

Joy is 16 and has the potential to become a professional violinist.
Insufficient funds and lack of self-belief were hindering Joy's musical
development; however an award from the Future Talent Bursary Scheme
and continuous support from the Charity have enabled her to flourish.
Joy now leads the Hallé Youth Orchestra, is a member of the National Youth
Orchestra and and plans to go to music college when she is 18...

"Future Talent has changed my life forever. It has inspired me to take all opportunities with both hands and go for anything no matter how daunting or impossible things may seem."

Future Talent gives financial awards and guidance to young musicians who are clearly demonstrating
outstanding musical ability or potential, but do not have the financial means to reach their goal.

Our Bursary Scheme is a vital resource and is funded by individuals who passionately believe in the
importance of providing the necessary stepping stones to allow young musicians to aim high and
make their musical dreams a reality.

For more information about funding opportunities and how
you can make a difference to the musical stars of tomorrow,
please get in touch.

we Find we Fund THEY FLOURISH

Future Talent, 33 Cavendish Square, London, W1G 0PW
T: 020 7182 4676 info@futuretalent.org www.futuretalent.org

Registered Charity No. 1107747

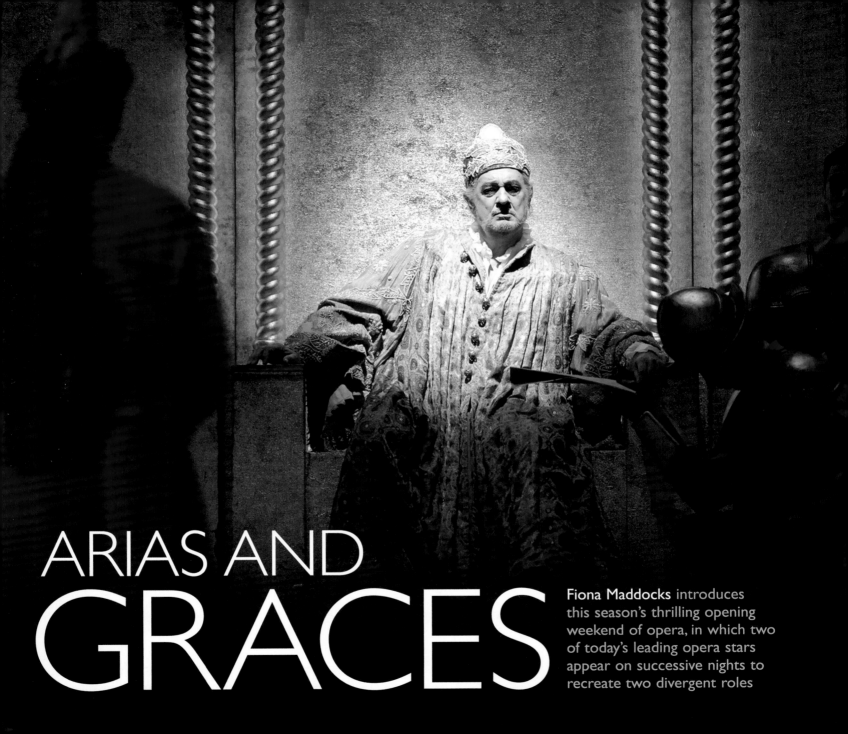

ARIAS AND
GRACES

Fiona Maddocks introduces this season's thrilling opening weekend of opera, in which two of today's leading opera stars appear on successive nights to recreate two divergent roles

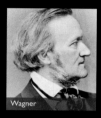

Wagner

Verdi

Humperdinck

With the glorious First Night panoply of Mahler's 'Symphony of a Thousand' still ringing in our ears, this season's blockbuster opening weekend continues with an operatic feast: two pinnacles of 19th-century opera, written by two mighty rivals known chiefly for their operatic output and sung by an array of international stars. In one, the cast is led by a megastar bass-baritone at the peak of his powers; in the other, by a globally acclaimed tenor in the Indian summer of his long career, enjoying new vitality in baritone repertoire.

On Saturday (17 July) Bryn Terfel performs the role of Hans Sachs, the visionary shoemaker in Wagner's *The Mastersingers of Nuremberg*, with the orchestra and chorus of Welsh National Opera conducted by their recently appointed music director, Lothar Koenigs. The following day Plácido Domingo performs the title-role in Verdi's *Simon Boccanegra* with the forces of the Royal Opera conducted by the company's music director, Antonio Pappano.

Wagner wrote *The Mastersingers* – the libretto *and* music – over a period of some 23 years from 1845, in between working on other operas, notably *Lohengrin*, *Tristan and Isolde* and his four-part *Ring* cycle. 'Certain good friends of mine …' he wrote in 1851, 'wished me to compose an opera of "lighter genre", since they believed that such a work would open the doors of most German theatres to me.' Eventually, and after many struggles and distractions, this would prove the case, not only in Germany but all over the world.

As its name suggests, *The Mastersingers* is an opera about music itself, with grand choruses, magnificent arias and a plot devised by the composer in this, his only comic work. A goldsmith's daughter, Eva, falls in love with a knight, Walther. But this being 16th-century Nuremberg, he can only win her hand by triumphing in the city's annual singing competition, held by the respected guild of Mastersingers. Old musical traditions vie with new, art with life

and love. In the midst of it all, Hans Sachs, Wagner's most generous-spirited and melancholy creation, casts wisdom and poetry around him.

The shoemaker was based on a real Hans Sachs (1494–1576), a Lutheran shoemaker, poet, playwright and leading Nuremberg 'Meistersinger'. Wagner makes him the central role in the opera, suited to bass, baritone or bass-baritone voice and on stage for most of the duration. As a philosopher and father figure also capable of mischief, he works to ensure that the lovers Eva and Walther will succeed in being united.

As a lonely widower, who harbours his own tender feelings for Eva and is capable of unkindness towards Walther's rival Beckmesser, Sachs struggles to understand his own purpose in life. He is, therefore, not merely a benign altruist, but a figure of conflicting, difficult feelings, with what Wagner's favourite philosopher, Schopenhauer, called a 'silent sadness' beneath the nobility. His huge, anguished aria 'Wahn' (meaning madness or delusion) in Act 3 Scene 1, pondering the folly of life and the nature of artistic inspiration, is at the heart of the opera. Bryn Terfel has recorded a searing account of this monologue, giving us a taste of the role he will sing for the first time this summer for Welsh National Opera.

Premiered in Munich in 1868, the opera was for Wagner a hymn to German art, a romanticising of an earlier Nuremberg, the city of Dürer and other masters of the Renaissance. For today's audience, because of its history in the 1930s, that city has taken on other, complex resonances. Wagner's 'national' opera has often been manipulated for other purposes. Yet its potent, overriding message, explored through more than four hours of impassioned and richly melodic music, is one of love, among humans both young and old, and towards homeland and art. Walther's 'Prize Song' witnesses the start of a new era. And yes, he gets his girl in the end.

Terfel's matchless bass-baritone is in prime condition for what he calls 'the torrential waters of Wagner', which now form his core repertoire. Two admired British artists, Amanda Roocroft as Eva and Christopher Purves as Beckmesser, join Terfel in an exciting cast.

Later in the season (1 August), Sir Simon Rattle conducts the period instruments of the Orchestra of the Age of ▶

FACING PAGE
Plácido Domingo combines private anguish and public duty in his role debut as Simon Boccanegra in the Berlin State Opera's production last October

BELOW
One of the great bass-baritones of our time, Bryn Terfel, as Wagner's wandering Wotan, in the Royal Opera's *Ring* cycle, 2004/5

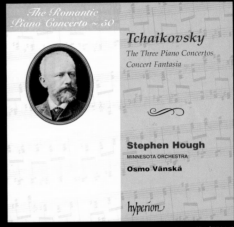

Plácido Domingo (*right*) sings the tenor role of Gabriele Adorno – the Doge's successor – alongside Kiri Te Kanawa's Amelia and Vladimir Chernov's Boccanegra, in the Act 3 finale of the Metropolitan Opera's *Simon Boccanegra*, 1995

Enlightenment in Act 2 of *Tristan and Isolde*, giving us the chance to find out what Wagner, in his self-reference via the character of Hans Sachs, meant by his words, 'My child, I know a sad tale of Tristan and Isolde. Hans Sachs is sensible and does not wish to share King Mark's fate.'

Born in 1813, the same year as Wagner, Verdi laboured for many years over *Simon Boccanegra*, widely regarded as one of his greatest masterpieces. As with *The Mastersingers*, this opera is set in an earlier age – 14th-century Genoa – but the politics of Italy in Verdi's own lifetime, in which he was deeply involved, are never far from mind. The casting is dark, with only the soprano Amelia – Boccanegra's 'lost' daughter (sung at the Proms by Marina Poplavskaya) – to offset the timbre of several male voices, including two baritones and two basses.

Performed here in the familiar revised 1881 version, *Boccanegra* embodies the composer's ongoing preoccupations: the relationship between a father and daughter and the responsibilities of power. The young corsair Simon Boccanegra, a plebeian, is nominated Doge to succeed his sworn enemy, the patrician Fiesco. Matters are not straightforward. Boccanegra loves Fiesco's daughter, Maria, with whom he has a child. At the moment he is elected, the crowds shouting his name in one of Verdi's most rousing choruses, he learns Maria is dead. And that's only the prologue. As the opera unfolds, we witness the unwilling, ageing Doge struggling with private loss, conscience and politics.

Domingo, who first sang the role in Berlin in October last year, has said that his desire to sing Boccanegra was primarily to do with loving the role, rather than wanting to sing baritone. He always imagined he would sing it late in his career, though to his surprise he's still combining it with tenor roles: 'I think that in any kind of career you can't keep doing the same over and over again, you have to look for new things … I'm always trying to find exciting parts,

either singing or conducting. It's really wonderful to be able to live all these unbelievable characters. And it's especially beautiful to suffer on stage! Something you don't like to do in life.'

Boccanegra certainly suffers, both personally and in public life. 'It's an exciting part, a noble character, with all the beautiful Verdi lines,' Domingo has observed. 'Strangely, it's perhaps the only baritone role in the whole of Verdi, along with Amonasro [from *Aida*], that doesn't really have an aria. But all his scenes are amazing, especially the great ensemble at the end of Act 1.'

The Proms opera feast does not stop there. On 31 August Robin Ticciati takes the baton for Humperdinck's fairy-tale opera *Hänsel and Gretel*, one of the best loved in the repertoire, full of recognisable tunes wrapped up in the capacious warmth of Wagner-inspired orchestration. The production, from this year's Glyndebourne Festival, stars Alice Coote and Lydia Teuscher as the siblings lost in the wood. And in this age of equal opportunity, tenor Wolfgang Ablinger-Sperrhacke gets into drag as the cruel Witch who, for all her hocus-pocus spells, ends up baked alive in her own oven, turned into gingerbread and good riddance. Let her eat cake. If any opera can cast a spell, this is it. ●

Chief Music Critic of *The Observer*, Fiona Maddocks was founder editor of *BBC Music Magazine* and has written a biography of the medieval visionary and composer Hildegard of Bingen.

'A Passion for Opera': look out for a series of new films, documentary and performance on BBC Two and BBC Four. BBC Radio 3 showcases productions from around the world and BBC Radio 2 searches the UK for a new opera star with Dame Kiri Te Kanawa. For more details, visit bbc.co.uk/opera.

Wolfgang Ablinger-Sperrhacke as the Witch in Glyndebourne's 2008 production of *Hänsel and Gretel*

OPERA AT THE PROMS

Prom 2, 17 July Wagner
The Mastersingers of Nuremberg
Orchestra and Chorus
of Welsh National Opera
Lothar Koenigs *conductor*

Prom 3, 18 July Verdi
Simon Boccanegra (1881 version)
Royal Opera Chorus
Orchestra of the Royal Opera House
Antonio Pappano *conductor*

Prom 21, 1 August
Wagner Tristan and Isolde – Act 2
Orchestra of the Age of Enlightenment
Sir Simon Rattle *conductor*

Prom 61, 31 August
Humperdinck Hänsel and Gretel
Glyndebourne Festival Opera,
London Philharmonic Orchestra
Robin Ticciati *conductor*

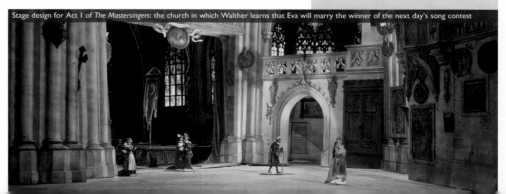

Stage design for Act 1 of *The Mastersingers*: the church in which Walther learns that Eva will marry the winner of the next day's song contest

Switch on.   Turn up.   Join in.

bbc.co.uk/tickets   bbc.co.uk/singers

EXTRAORDINARILY TALENTED PEOPLE

ROYAL COLLEGE OF MUSIC, LONDON

020 7589 3643

www.rcm.ac.uk

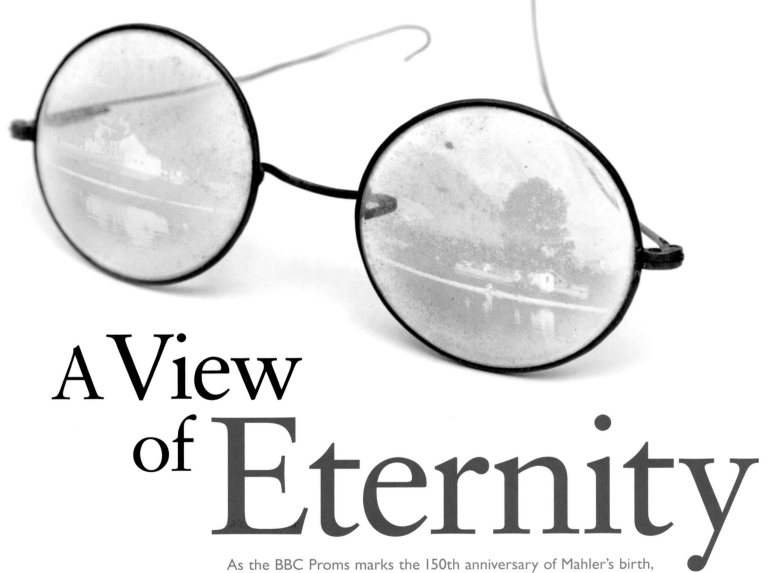

A View of Eternity

As the BBC Proms marks the 150th anniversary of Mahler's birth, Henry-Louis de La Grange outlines the universal themes of human existence and the world beyond that inspired the composer to produce orchestral scores of unprecedented reach and scale

Throughout his life Mahler was attacked and pilloried for the contradictions inherent in his music, a feature which we now recognise as the hallmark of his genius. His music has often seemed shocking, paradoxical, even 'scandalous' (a quality which time and familiarity have tended to make us forget). And yet, if we want to understand it and appreciate it fully, Mahler's music should never strike us as reassuring. It should sound eternally new, challenging and provoking the listener as it did in its own day, when it seemed to fly in the face of received ideas, unbending rules and all the criteria governing good taste and common sense.

If Mahler's music is both personal and universal, it is not only because he poured himself into it with all his own ambiguities and contradictions, but also because he was able to turn his raw material into consummate art without ever sacrificing the richness of his inner world. His works do not distinguish between dreams and reality, but strive to bring the two worlds into alignment. Mahler used his own being – his experiences, his philosophical speculations and the visions that seized him – as the living matter of his art, yet much of his music defies explanation, a point he himself made on more than one occasion: 'What matters above all in a work of art is that it contains an element of mystery, something that baffles the intellect and defies analysis.' For Mahler, musical creation was 'an essentially mystical act': 'Without knowing it, one often constructs something that one is no longer able to understand once the work has come into the world … It sometimes happens that you are led by a mysterious, unconscious force.'

Throughout his life Mahler was fascinated by the mysteries of art and the human condition as well as by the idea of the hereafter. All his close friends stressed this fundamental aspect of his character. The conductor Oskar Fried noted:

> He was a man in search of God. With unparalleled fervour, unique dedication and unshakeable love he sought the divine in man, in each of us. He saw himself as an emissary of God and was wholly imbued by his mission. His was an essentially religious nature in the mystical, rather than the dogmatic, sense of the term.

Having become a composer, such a man could not be content with mere note-spinning or even with expressing his own particular states of mind. He owed it to himself to embrace the act of musical creation with proselytising zeal, and to commit himself to it body and soul. Throughout his life he refused persistently, categorically and viscerally

Programme cover for performances at the Concertgebouw, Amsterdam (22 & 23 October 1903), conducted by Mahler

His works do not distinguish between dreams and reality, but strive to bring the two worlds into alignment.

to accept the materialism and rationalism of his time, the later 19th century. For this reason his thinking remained basically optimistic – because the 'here-below' was always a reflection of the beyond and because he never ceased to believe in an afterlife, a belief that was as much a part of his life as it was of his music.

In a letter written only days before his death, Goethe had argued that the principal meaning of *Faust* could be summed up in these lines:

> *He who, always striving, toils –*
> *him we can redeem.*

For Faust, then, activity was more important than love, the quest more crucial than the conquest. For Mahler, too, activity was the principal law of life: it is up to us to forge our own destiny, a point ▶

UNIQUE HOME STAYS

wake up somewhere different...

www.uniquehomestays.com

Dem lieben treuen Freunde Sektionsrath Dr. ...ald ...ek

Wien, Dezember 1907

Gustav Mahler

> Mahler's music is both the most personal and one of the most universal there is, and that is why it cannot leave us indifferent … It remains indefinable because it contains all that constitutes the world and humankind.

that emerges from the lines he added to those of Klopstock at the end of his 'Resurrection' Symphony (No. 2):

> *With wings that I have won myself,*
> *I shall soar aloft*
> *in love's ardent striving.*

In his Eighth Symphony, Mahler would later echo Goethe in preaching the dynamic virtues that he himself always practised: an impulsive striving for the infinite, even if that impulse leads to error; purification through experience; victory over ourselves; acceptance of life and its limitations; the sanctification of practical activity geared to a specific goal; solidarity between human beings; and, finally, love as the utopian law in the world.

As a result, Mahler's music is both the most personal and one of the most universal there is, and that is why it cannot leave us indifferent. It is paradoxical, ambiguous and sometimes even inscrutable. It captivates us and slips through our fingers, it is troubling and calming, both overwhelming us and smiling upon us. It spurs

us on unceasingly, forcing us to ask questions both about the music and about ourselves, including our surroundings and our future. It remains indefinable because it contains all that constitutes the world and humankind: compassion and derision, beauty and ugliness, faith and doubt, lyricism and violence, subjectivity and objectivity, the sublime and the everyday, the eternal and the ephemeral, intuition and reflection, epic heroism and intimate confidence.

It is uniquely sincere and ambiguous, not least because it reflects the ambiguities of human nature – especially those of 20th-century men and women who have recognised the impossibility of achieving any reassuring synthesis, and discovered that the most basic truths can always be upturned. Each affirmative statement is called into question by an element of irony. This music accepts the limitations, weaknesses and vicissitudes of the human condition and with exemplary honesty recognises that life is made up of contradictions.

Mahler is great precisely because he contradicts himself and knows that certitude comes only after a bitter struggle (and that it may yet be lost again). He teaches us that we are forever being confronted ▶

A window by Edward Burne-Jones (1833–98), featuring St Cecilia flanked by angels. Her powers to raise the spirits are evoked in the depiction of heavenly life that forms the last movement of Mahler's Fourth Symphony

MAHLER IN OUR TIME

Marina Mahler is the granddaughter of Gustav Mahler and his wife Alma. She actively participates and promotes the work of her grandfather, taking part in numerous events around the world.

What would Mahler think of our world today?

Since his death …
Two World Wars and countless instances
    of genocide …

What would the music sound like …?
I have often wondered …

And the slow, irrevocable destruction of our planet,
Of its delicate and perfect checks and balances …
How would he –
Who so lived nature,
Who depended on it for healing all the inner human
    pains and memories,
For his creative energies and rhythms,
– How would he have felt about these balances
    being irrevocably altered and endangered?

Of all the music ever written, his seems to have
    intimated so much of what was to come.
The relief we feel listening to his music today,
    is because of his deep inner vision.
His emotions capture the feelings of today,
Give them scope and meaning,
Give them an outlet.
A truly contemporary composer, his vision stands
    for the now we are worriedly living.

When I go to a concert of contemporary music
And the music seems to me not really new,
But a little nostalgic or sentimental,
Then I think to myself …
What would he have
Written now?
What truths would he have felt?

And I go to each concert of contemporary music
Hoping to find something of the scale and impact
    which we need and search for –
Which can contain and explode, or relieve, what we
    are living now,

What we are anticipating of our world …
For our future.

Our hearts break when politics fail,
When ideals break down,
When dreams are not lived up to …

We need a kind of music to revive the heart …
To warm and strengthen it again …
We should all search more!

Somewhere there will be a young composer
    whom we don't yet know,
Whose work will lift the spirit,
Make us touch base amid all the fruitless haste
Which we insist upon.
It is important to listen,
To be open to new sounds and new ways,
In the hope that we discover something
Which will bowl us over by its force and truth.

In these two important Mahler (anniversary) years,
I feel this would be the truest homage one
    could give …
To go in search of new beauties,
New sounds …
New visions …
And to do all one can to save Nature as we know it,
So that it may give strength to those not yet born.

If one truly loves someone's work, one should give
    time and thought to the things which inspired it,
Understanding that these are precious objects
Which need our attention and our love,
Our recognition and our sustenance.
For future generations …
Only in this way is death bearable,
Thinking that all we hold beautiful will
Go on existing.

by uncertainties which extend beyond the here and now and by a mystery that is the mystery of life. His music speaks to us of suffering because suffering is an integral part of life; it also speaks of death because only the prospect of death can give meaning and value to life. In this way it offers us reassurance in the form of the responses that Mahler was convinced came from beyond.

As a Jew, finding himself at the crossroads of several civilisations, he was constantly torn between the conflicting aspirations of his Jewish identity and the desire to be assimilated: he both observed the world from afar and engaged with it. Sometimes his gaze would acquire a sense of distance, becoming frighteningly cold and harsh. His marginalised position, of which he often complained, ▶

Mahler walking to the Vienna Court Opera, where he was director (photograph c1904)

RSC
ROYAL
SHAKESPEARE
COMPANY

KING LEAR

ROMEO AND JULIET

HAMLET

MORTE D' ARTHUR
THE LEGEND
OF KING ARTHUR &
HIS KNIGHTS OF THE ROUND TABLE

ANTONY AND CLEOPATRA

FEBRUARY-SEPTEMBER 2010
WWW.RSC.ORG.UK
(NO BOOKING FEE)

0844 800 1110
(NO BOOKING FEE; CALLS FROM A BT LANDLINE COST 5P PER MINUTE)

TICKETS FROM £12

accenture

ARTS COUNCIL ENGLAND

Supported by
ARTS COUNCIL
ENGLAND

was the source of this rigorous objectivity, coexisting in him with the subjectivity of the poet and the musician. He was never satisfied with reassuring certainties or with easily won victories. While fuelling his endless uncertainty, this marginalisation was perhaps his greatest strength, giving rise above all to the irony that created a distance between subject and object.

Mahler's final works breathe a new kind of certainty, ending his huge symphonic novel – nine symphonies plus an incomplete tenth – in catharsis, fulfilment and sublimation. However, the earlier chapters were replete with 'sound and fury' and, long before soaring up to the vertiginous heights of those late codas, Mahler had already twice affirmed his profound belief in transcendence: in the triumphal assertion of faith during the final bars of the Third Symphony; and in the equally moving *pianissimo* conclusion of the third movement of his next and sister-work, the Fourth – a blissful ascending melody leading to the 'heavenly life' of the song-finale. Neither of these two codas should ever fail to bring tears to the listener's eyes. ●

Henry-Louis de La Grange is one of the world's leading Mahler scholars. The long-awaited fourth volume of his Mahler biography was published in 2008. He is President of the Médiathèque Musicale Mahler, Paris.

Etching by Emil Orlik (1870–1932)

A graphic portrait by Rainer Ehrt (born 1960) showing Mahler in a Viennese alley

MAHLER AT THE PROMS

Des Knaben Wunderhorn – selection
Prom 18, 30 July

Lieder eines fahrenden Gesellen
Prom 62, 1 September

Manfred – overture (Schumann, orch. Mahler)
Prom 4, 19 July

Rückert-Lieder
Prom 48, 21 August

Symphony No. 1 in D major
Prom 65, 3 September

Symphony No. 3 in D minor
Prom 24, 4 August

Symphony No. 4 in G major
Prom 26, 5 August

Symphony No. 5 in C sharp minor
Prom 26, 5 August

Symphony No. 7
Prom 34, 10 August

Symphony No. 8 in E flat major, 'Symphony of a Thousand'
Prom 1, 16 July

Mahler rehearsing large forces for the premiere in Munich of his Symphony No. 8, 'Symphony of a Thousand', 12 September 1910

BBC National Orchestra of Wales

BBC

Get closer to the music

Aberystwyth / Bangor / Bradford-on-Avon
Brecon / Cardiff / Cheltenham / London
Llandudno / Newtown / St Asaph
St Davids / Swansea / Wrexham

CALL FOR DETAILS OF OUR 2010 / 11 SEASON

BBC National Orchestra of Wales Audience Line   **0800 052 1812**   bbc.co.uk/now

BOX OFFICE
0121 780 3333
www.thsh.co.uk

BIRMINGHAM INTERNATIONAL CONCERT SEASON 2010/11

On sale late April

Piotr Anderszewski, Daniel Barenboim, Cecilia Bartoli, Beijing Symphony Orchestra, Il Giardino Armonico, Houston Symphony/NASA, London Symphony Orchestra with Valery Gergiev, James MacMillan, Santa Cecilia Orchestra with Antonio Pappano, Philharmonia Orchestra with Esa-Pekka Salonen, CBSO with Sir Simon Rattle, Andreas Scholl, Takács Quartet, Mitsuko Uchida.

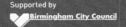

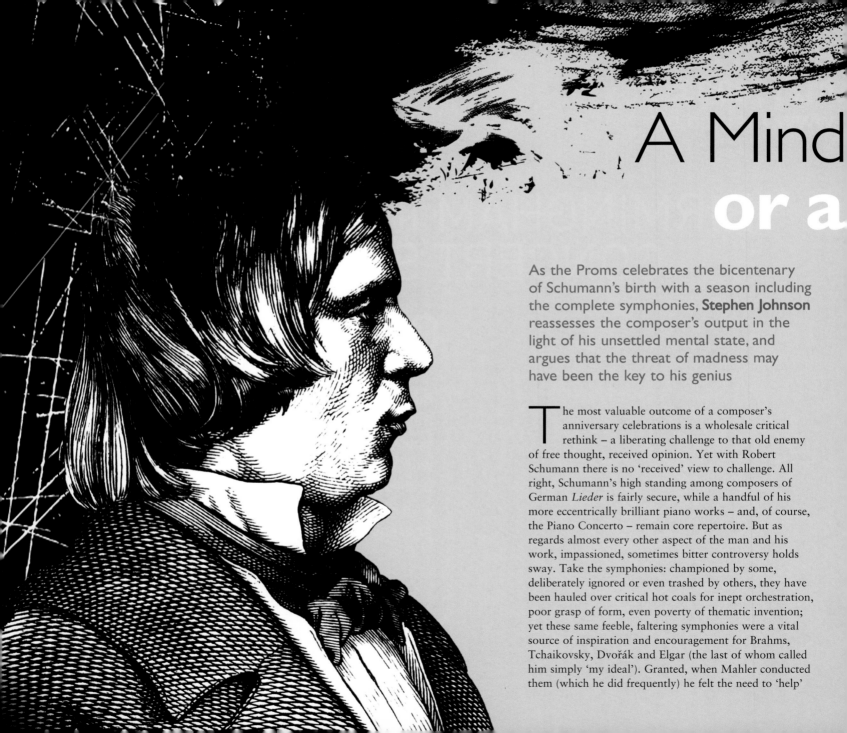

A Mind

or a

As the Proms celebrates the bicentenary
of Schumann's birth with a season including
the complete symphonies, **Stephen Johnson**
reassesses the composer's output in the
light of his unsettled mental state, and
argues that the threat of madness may
have been the key to his genius

The most valuable outcome of a composer's
anniversary celebrations is a wholesale critical
rethink – a liberating challenge to that old enemy
of free thought, received opinion. Yet with Robert
Schumann there is no 'received' view to challenge. All
right, Schumann's high standing among composers of
German *Lieder* is fairly secure, while a handful of his
more eccentrically brilliant piano works – and, of course,
the Piano Concerto – remain core repertoire. But as
regards almost every other aspect of the man and his
work, impassioned, sometimes bitter controversy holds
sway. Take the symphonies: championed by some,
deliberately ignored or even trashed by others, they have
been hauled over critical hot coals for inept orchestration,
poor grasp of form, even poverty of thematic invention;
yet these same feeble, faltering symphonies were a vital
source of inspiration and encouragement for Brahms,
Tchaikovsky, Dvořák and Elgar (the last of whom called
him simply 'my ideal'). Granted, when Mahler conducted
them (which he did frequently) he felt the need to 'help'

Unhinged ...
Genius Unlocked?

Interfoto/Mary Evans Picture Library (p34); akg-images (below right)

the orchestration – but then he did the same with Beethoven and Schubert, whom we're somewhat less inclined to help nowadays.

As more and more of Schumann's music has re-emerged (or in some cases simply emerged) from obscurity in recent years, reaction has once again become polarised. For some, the cello and violin concertos, the choral-orchestral *Das Paradies und die Peri*, the *Scenes from Goethe's 'Faust'* and the

Was Schumann manic-depressive ... or was it syphilis that finally upturned his brain and sentenced him to spend his last two years in a lunatic asylum?

three string quartets are exquisitely original, any putative faults utterly eclipsed by their many precious and unique virtues. For others, they are simply sad failures, in some cases painful testimony to Schumann's increasingly delusional state as he approached his final mental collapse.

And there, the biggest, nastiest can of worms opens irrevocably. Did Schumann suffer from mental illness? If so, was it continuous, intermittent or only really manifest in his last decade? Was he manic-depressive (or, as we'd now say, bipolar), or was it syphilis that finally upturned his brain and sentenced him to spend

his last two years in a lunatic asylum? Bizarrely, many of the commentators who have weighed in on the last issue (see, for instance, John Worthen's recent *Robert Schumann: Life and Death of a Musician*) seem to be convinced that it has to be one or the other – can't a manic-depressive *also* catch syphilis? Until the final years Schumann's creative life shows the kind of extreme undulating pattern typical of many bipolar creative people: periods of intense mental activity and artistic productivity (for example, the 'wonder years' 1840–43 following his marriage to Clara Wieck) alternating with long periods of depression and anxiety in which virtually nothing is produced (1844 and early 1845). But many artists and thinkers manage to survive the highs and lows and continue producing great work over long, full lives – in some cases it is clear that their creativity was a major force in keeping them stable enough to continue. Might Schumann have done the same, if syphilis hadn't been added to an already dangerous mixture?

What is quite clear in reading books, articles and reviews dealing with this issue in relation to Schumann is that a huge weight of prejudice still bears down on many attempts at rational discussion. First, to say that someone 'suffers from

mental illness' is emphatically not the same as saying that they are permanently 'mentally ill' – still less 'mad' – any more than to say that someone is physically 'ill' implies that they should be booking themselves into a hospice. The mental health charity MIND estimates that around one in four adults suffers from depression at some time in their lives; yet for most of their lives the majority of these people will function perfectly normally. Secondly, however enlightened we may claim to be, it is clear that many educated people still cling, if unconsciously, to the Victorian belief that ▶

The house in Zwickau, Saxony, where Robert Schumann was born and brought up

The title-page of a piano-duet edition of Schumann's Fourth Symphony

mental illness is basically a 'moral' disorder. One reviewer of John Worthen's book enthusiastically hailed its rejection of the deplorable suggestion that Schumann suffered from a mental illness, yet seemed to have no difficulty accommodating himself to the book's portrayal of the composer as a syphilitic drunk.

Part of the problem surely derives from another popularly persisting 19th-century notion: that of the tortured 'mad genius' – usually backed up with a well-worn phrase like 'genius is close to madness'. Actually the history of that saying is rather interesting. It appears to derive from a once frequently quoted couplet in John Dryden's poem *Absalom and Achitophel*: 'Great wits are sure to madness near allied, / And thin partitions do their bounds divide.' What is striking about Dryden's version is that he sees great creative intelligence as *near* to madness, not congruent with it: the two states are separated by 'thin partitions'. The point is surely that the partitions are thin enough to allow the artist to see into the unconscious, nocturnal regions of the mind that emerge unmediated in madness, but that they still remain strong enough to prevent him from being overwhelmed. The tiny boat exposes the navigator to the full terror and exhilaration of the storm-tossed sea, yet remains just sturdy enough to remain afloat. As the eminent psychiatrist and amateur musician Anthony Storr forcefully pointed out, truly psychotic art is often very boring. When the rational conscious mind, the 'ego', is completely overwhelmed, its utterances tend to become repetitive, stilted, formulaic and full of the kind of dissociated imagery that makes sense only to the sufferer – and, perhaps, to the patient, empathic psychiatrist.

In which case, the fact that Schumann's most emotionally extreme, intellectually paradoxical compositions clearly do make sense to large numbers of listeners has to be an indication that their composer remained basically stable at the time he wrote them. His rope was long and supple enough to allow him to descend into the subterranean dream-world, but strong enough to pull him back, with the otherworldly treasures he found safely in his knapsack. The hushed 'fantasy' episode at the heart of the Piano Concerto's first movement or the delicious, timeless flute cadenza in the finale of the First Symphony are two of the most obvious and attractive examples.

But we can also see evidence of this in the brilliantly 'lateral' structures he created in some of his most original works. In the Second Symphony, the work Schumann composed to pull himself back out of the crippling depression of 1844–5, the manic, obsessive, driven repetitions of the first two movements are calmed by the wonderful invocation of Bach – in Goethe's words, the portrayer of 'the eternal harmony' – in the minor-key Adagio. The latter ends peacefully, but the turbulent finale is haunted by memories of its darkly eloquent lyricism, eventually leading to a kind of grim 'alternative' ending – after which the finale begins again with new material: a sort of structural 'take 2'. Schumann seems to present us with two possible outcomes: one hopeful, the other tragic. The Fourth Symphony (actually composed before No. 2, but revised later) takes this kind of lateral structural thinking to levels of almost

The fact that Schumann's most emotionally extreme, intellectually paradoxical compositions clearly do make sense to large numbers of listeners has to be an indication that their composer remained basically stable at the time he wrote them.

Escher-like complexity. For a start, is the symphony in four movements, or one? Apparently audience and critics at the first performance found it just too confusing. But, for those who don't need their symphonies neatly laid out, the Fourth Symphony's ambiguity is its glory. After the 'second' movement's gorgeous oboe and solo cello tune, the shadowy slow introduction of the first movement is heard again: is this a flashback or a new theme within the context of a new movement? This ambiguous formal gamesmanship continues in the Scherzo. The listener may even wonder if two simultaneous strands of argument are unfolding here, one fleetingly intruding on the other like a visitor from a parallel world.

Significantly, when Schumann revised this symphony nearly a decade later, and three years before his final breakdown, he seems to have taken fright at some of these manifestations of lateral fantasy. Schumann sometimes went to quite radical lengths to make the formal outlines clearer, most drastically in the transition between the finale's slow introduction and main allegro. Where in the first version the introduction eventually boils over and sweeps on into the finale, the revision draws itself up and pauses grandly, like a master of ceremonies portentously announcing, 'And now, ladies and gentlemen, the finale!' Of course Schumann may simply have wanted to guarantee his most original symphony an easier ride with audience and critics, but to this writer these revisions betray an element of panic. Are the 'thin partitions' too thin after all: do they need strengthening? Better safe than sorry – or perhaps not.

It is quite true that Schumann was able to achieve mastery within more apparently stable, conventionally rounded forms. The magnificent *Manfred* overture breaks no significant structural rules, allows no guests from parallel universes (though the oddly syncopated opening chords have puzzled some conductors) and its tragic emotional intensity is surely only enhanced by the strength of its formal 'container'. Composed in Düsseldorf where Schumann had become municipal music director, the Third Symphony (1850) manages to incorporate a substantial extra movement – an atmospheric evocation of a solemn ceremony witnessed in Cologne Cathedral – in the process only strengthening the symphony's overall architectural plan. The Piano Quintet is one of Schumann's most admired large-scale compositions, yet its apparent formal security – rounded off by an elegantly solid fugue – conceals more intriguingly lateral touches: for instance, another quiet 'flashback' in the funereal slow movement to a fleeting passage midway through the first. And what of the funeral march itself:

is it grief-laden or mischievously ironic – or both?

Schumann will always frustrate those who like their ambiguities resolved, their endings reassuringly closed, their emotions formally tamed. He will continue to draw scorn from those who see the ultimate manifestation of 'art' in a polished surface. For others, though, like this writer, he is at his greatest the embodiment of what John Keats called 'negative capability': the ability to exist 'in uncertainties, mysteries, doubts, without any irritable reaching after fact and reason'. Approach Schumann in a similar frame of mind and his unique, multi-faceted mastery should be apparent at every beguiling twist and turn. ●

Stephen Johnson has written regularly for The Independent, The Guardian and BBC Music Magazine, and is the author of books on Bruckner, Mahler and Wagner. He is a regular presenter of BBC Radio 3's Discovering Music.

Düsseldorf – where Schumann wrote his 'Rhenish' Symphony in 1850 – viewed from the Rhine

SCHUMANN AT THE PROMS

Dichterliebe, Op. 48
Proms Chamber Music 1, 19 July

Introduction and Allegro appassionato in G major, Op. 92 Prom 74, 9 September

Liederkreis, Op. 24
Proms Saturday Matinee 4, 28 August

Manfred – overture (orch. Mahler) Prom 4, 19 July

Overture, Scherzo and Finale, Op. 52
Prom 12, 25 July

Piano Concerto in A minor Prom 12, 25 July

Piano Quartet in E flat major, Op. 47
Proms Saturday Matinee 4, 28 August

Piano Quintet in E flat major, Op. 44
Proms Chamber Music 2, 26 July

Symphony in G minor, 'Zwickau' (incomplete)
Prom 51, 23 August

Symphony No. 1 in B flat major, 'Spring'
Prom 13, 26 July

Symphony No. 2 in C major Prom 51, 23 August

Symphony No. 3 in E flat major, 'Rhenish'
Prom 15, 28 July

Symphony No. 4 in D minor (revised version)
Prom 37, 13 August

See also:

Robin Holloway Fantasy-Pieces
(on the Heine 'Liederkreis' of Schumann)
Proms Saturday Matinee 4, 20 August

Robin Holloway RELIQUARY: Scenes from the life of Mary, Queen of Scots, enclosing an instrumentation of Schumann's 'Gedichte der Königin Maria Stuart'
BBC commission: world premiere
Prom 74, 9 September

JOIN US...

AND BE THE FIRST TO HEAR ABOUT OUR CONCERTS, BROADCASTS & ACTIVITIES

Supported by

Salford City Council

BBC RADIO
90 – 93FM

CHANDOS

Visit us anytime at bbc.co.uk/philharmonic
e. philharmonic@bbc.co.uk   t. 0161 244 4001

The Spirit of
BEETHOVEN

Paul Lewis, who plays all five of Beethoven's piano concertos at the Proms this season, offers his own view of these endlessly varied masterpieces

Beethoven's association with the piano concerto dates back as far as 1784, with an early concerto in E flat of which only the piano part survives today. This juvenile work may not fully anticipate his later achievements, but it nevertheless displays a confident and athletic style of piano writing – the 13-year-old composer evidently saw no reason to hold back from demonstrating his already considerable pianistic abilities. Later that decade, around 1788, Beethoven turned his attention to a concerto in B flat – a work he would revise many times, even replacing the finale, before its publication in 1801. This is the work we know as the Second Piano Concerto, even though the C major work which we recognise as 'No. 1' originated some years later.

However, it is the three great concertos that followed in the first decade of the 19th century that have come most characteristically to represent Beethoven's contribution to the genre. In these works we see new ground constantly being broken, new rules created (sometimes only to be rudely discarded further down the line) and new depths of expression explored with a combination of unyielding determination and heartfelt honesty.

Although essentially different in character, the first two concertos share a feeling of youthful fearlessness, fused with an already impressive mastery of material and its development. There is a sure-footed sense of direction, a touch of impulsiveness here and there and, above all, a genuine sense of fun. The First Concerto in particular conveys a real sense of pianistic revelry. The piano's first entry quickly establishes the solo role as one of unrestrained virtuosity, with some brilliantly tempestuous passagework. The eccentric (at times manic) cadenza Beethoven supplied some years later goes even further in extending the virtuoso element, climaxing in a frenzy of cascading *fortissimo* chords which seem alarmingly insane. Inevitably, it's not long before this tips over into brusque humour, with one or two passages that require almost as much acting as piano playing. Even at this early stage the bluntness of Beethoven's humour presents itself as one of his most distinctive features.

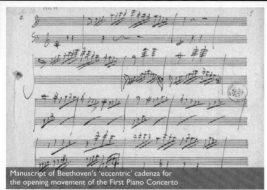

Manuscript of Beethoven's 'eccentric' cadenza for the opening movement of the First Piano Concerto

Bibliothèque National de France/Giraudon/Bridgeman Art Library (p+0, inset); H. C. Bodmer collection/Beethoven-Haus, Bonn (below left)

In these works we see new ground constantly being broken, new rules created and new depths of expression explored with unyielding determination and heartfelt honesty.

If the First Concerto reaches out to the listener with bold directness, the Second chooses a more understated route. Here there's a Mozartian lyricism, and a playfulness which in some ways points back to Haydn, the master of mischief. Though the slow movement is rooted in rhetorical pathos, it never strays too far from the geniality that underpins the work as a whole, while the rondo finale bounds along without a care in the world. As with the First Concerto, Beethoven added a first-movement cadenza long after the work's premiere, although this time the character is rugged, gnarly and obsessive – entirely at odds with rest of the work. Beethoven had earlier been dismissive of this concerto, but one assumes he must have revised his former doubts to have bothered writing a cadenza of such substance. In any case, it is during these three highly charged minutes that the landscape bizarrely turns on its head. The fingers are twisted into contortions and the ears are forced to adjust to a more shocking sound-world that almost anticipates the 'Hammerklavier' Sonata of almost a decade later. It took me some time to come to terms with this mood swing. For a few years I played my own evolving attempts at a cadenza, venturing to imitate what Beethoven might have written at the time he completed the work, in the mid-1790s. I then tried playing his later cadenza in a way that made it sound stylistically closer to the rest of the piece. Nowadays, I simply play the cadenza as it is. It adds a different dimension to the work, shocking in many ways, but it nevertheless tells us something unique and valuable about Beethoven's character.

The Third Concerto is a pivotal work in the cycle – a clear turning point in the development of Beethoven's musical language. The boldness of character of the themes, with which Beethoven is so associated, is as much in evidence here as anywhere: realising this in performance is the key to allowing Beethoven's keen structural logic to speak for itself. A subdued sense of unease and mystery in the opening bars sets the scene for a movement packed with tension and binds those inexorable Beethovenian structural blocks persuasively together. In this work we encounter a composer in total command of the unfolding of his argument, to the point where the first-movement cadenza is no longer left to the whim of the performer – for the first time it is written out in the score. As if to leave us in no doubt that this is integral to the movement's structure, Beethoven makes a point of shifting the main climax into the cadenza itself. The test for the pianist is to pace the momentum in a way that makes this summit unmistakably clear, while being careful not to dilute any of the music's natural volatility or drive. If the shape of the first movement is ▶

Interior of the Beethoven-Haus, Bonn, showing Beethoven's last fortepiano, loaned to the composer by the Viennese maker Conrad Graf in 1826

convincingly managed, then the solitary radiance of the slow movement effortlessly takes its place as an oasis of calm between two turbulent landscapes. This mood of tranquillity presents itself as another challenge towards the end of the rondo finale, when the major-key tonality of the slow movement is recalled. The restless character of the rondo's main theme has somehow to be combined with a frozen-in-time memory of the slow movement's E major colour – a moment which should turn out to be as icy as it is dream-like.

The Fourth Concerto has always stood out to me as the most demanding of the cycle. The warm, intimate character of the first movement disguises a structural layout that is the most daringly unorthodox of the set in its fluidity. Shunning the more extrovert traits of some of its siblings, it explores a more personal world and does so with a movingly heartfelt depth. Tenderness, intimacy and sheer beauty are the qualities which are most immediately apparent, although a typically steely Beethovenian core reveals itself from time to time. In performance, one needs a high level of understanding between pianist and conductor, a sensitivity to balancing orchestral colour with that of the piano, an elasticity of pulse enabling the slightest changes of tempo to sound naturally connected to the music's character, and a genuine understanding of the relationship between the work's outer tenderness and underlying intensity. All of these qualities also need to be felt unanimously by around 70 musicians! Where the other concertos perhaps reach out more directly, the Fourth discreetly draws its audience in. As we hear most clearly in the slow movement, the emotional power of introspection has no problem asserting itself over physical force. Perhaps that tells us something about the work as a whole.

Finally, to the most famous concerto of the set, nicknamed the 'Emperor'. True, majesty, grandeur and physical excitement are essential parts of what this piece conveys, but it would be wrong to imagine that this represents the full picture. I have to admit to being rather sceptical about the value of such labels: there's a danger that the music is perceived in a way that justifies the title, rather than the other way round. More intriguing, for a work of such epic proportions, is the constant recurrence of passages which are quintessentially chamber-like in their intimacy. I believe one of the most important keys to a satisfying performance lies in the management of these delicate and often fragile balances. To convey intimacy on a chamber-like scale within a symphonic context, and to do it convincingly in a large hall, is far from easy. It's as important to be constantly alive to the balance of the piano with a single wind instrument or with a hushed pizzicato passage, as it is to rise above the colossal sound of the orchestra in the places that require it. Pianistic virtuosity undeniably has a role to play, but it's of a kind which serves the core of what the music expresses. For instance, the finale certainly needs fire, but it's important to remember that this is dance music, and dancers – perhaps even more than pianists – need space to breathe.

Each of Beethoven's five piano concertos inhabits its own unique world: from the infectious enthusiasm of the two early works to the military resilience of the 'Emperor', via the rarefied world of the Fourth Concerto. Beethoven sees no reason to repeat himself and presents the performer with a whole range of challenges endlessly rich in interpretative possibilities. While these works might not provide a comprehensive view of the man behind them, they certainly offer a vivid and powerful snapshot of that most intractable of musical personalities. ●

Relief by E. Koch after a drawing by August von Kloeber

PAUL LEWIS PLAYS BEETHOVEN'S PIANO CONCERTOS AT THE PROMS

Piano Concerto No. 1 in C major Prom 6, 21 July

Piano Concerto No. 2 in B flat major Prom 16, 29 July

Piano Concerto No. 3 in C minor Prom 27, 6 August

Piano Concerto No. 4 in G major Prom 6, 21 July

Piano Concerto No. 5 in E flat major, 'Emperor'
Prom 69, 6 September

Join the BBC Symphony Chorus

One of the UK's finest and most distinctive amateur choirs, the BBC Symphony Chorus was founded in 1928. In its appearances with the BBC Symphony Orchestra, the chorus performs a wide range of challenging repertoire which is usually broadcast on BBC Radio 3. As resident chorus for the BBC Proms, the chorus takes part in a number of concerts each season, including the Last Night. This year's appearances include Mahler's Symphony No. 8 at the First Night, a 'solo' Prom under Chorus Director Stephen Jackson and Bartók's *Cantata Profana* with the BBC Symphony Orchestra under David Robertson.

2010–11 Season Highlights

Highlights of the 2010–11 season at the Barbican with the BBC SO include Delius's *Song of the High Hills* conducted by Sir Andrew Davis, Julian Anderson's *Heaven is Shy of Earth* with Oliver Knussen, Rachmaninov's *The Bells* with Semyon Bychkov and music by some of the great Hollywood composers.

Would you like to join us?

If you are an experienced choral singer who would like to work on new and challenging repertoire, as well as standard choral works, then the BBC Symphony Chorus would like to hear from you. Membership is free and includes individual vocal training as well as the opportunity to work with world-class conductors and soloists alongside the BBC Symphony Orchestra at the Barbican and Proms. Enquiries from altos and basses are especially welcome.

To find out more about the Chorus, or to apply for an audition, visit **bbc.co.uk/symphonyorchestra** or contact the Chorus Administrator.
Email: bbcsc@bbc.co.uk
Tel: 020 7765 4715

Open Rehearsal
Saturday 29 May 2010

The BBC Symphony Chorus would like to invite experienced singers who may be interested in auditioning for the Chorus to join them for the day as they begin rehearsing Mahler's Symphony No. 8 in preparation for the First Night of the Proms. For more information visit bbc.co.uk/symphonyorchestra or email **bbcsc@bbc.co.uk**

BBC RADIO 3

90–93 FM

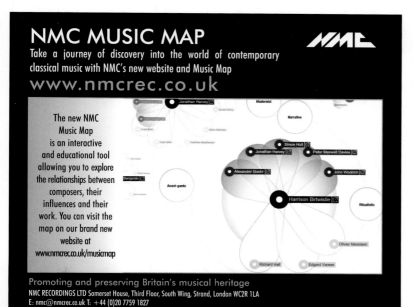

Coloured Ambition

Cosseted from infancy by doting relatives, it was little wonder that Alexander Scriabin became the centre of his own world. Jonathan Powell traces how the composer's mystical philosophies and sensual scores were part of a high-minded goal to transfigure humanity

The Moscow Conservatory, where Scriabin studied from 1888 to 1892, proving himself to be a gifted pianist

A Parisian critic of the 1890s labelled Alexander Scriabin a 'Russian Chopin' – early works such as the Piano Concerto certainly have a delicacy and intimacy that make little attempt to disguise this debt. But Scriabin soon outgrew both Chopin's and Wagner's influences, and by the early 20th century he was writing works of energetic daring, of ultra-vivid colours and mystical content. When composing the *The Poem of Ecstasy* (his fourth symphony, 1905–8), Scriabin enthused that the work would be 'a great joy, an enormous festival'; this concept of music as a participatory act of artistic and spiritual celebration was central to his approach. By the end of his short life (1872–1915) Scriabin had developed a revolutionary new musical language that would complement his plans to transfigure humanity with an apocalyptic work: the unfinished *Mysterium*, incorporating music, words, dance, lights and incense.

Scriabin's mother, Lyubov Petrovna Shchetinina, was one of the first recognised female musicians in Russia, a pianist and composer who had garnered high praise from Tchaikovsky. She even gave a virtuoso recital days before Scriabin was born, on Christmas Day 1871 (by the 'old style' Julian calendar). Her death just over a year later meant that Scriabin was raised by female relatives, who

spoilt him and certainly fed his later egocentricity. He studied the piano alongside Rachmaninov and Goldenweiser, and their teacher Nikolay Zverev also introduced his pupils to foreign languages, manners of high society, and great literature. In 1887 Scriabin started to write poems that spiritually coexisted as literary equivalents of particular compositions, as well as compiling his meditations regarding religion. He became one of the Moscow Conservatory's foremost piano students, but lived much of the 1890s on a Dostoyevskyan knife-edge, precipitously close to breakdown. He also gained the habit of staying out drinking all night, a tendency which increased before subsiding in later years.

The patron and publisher Mitrofan Belyayev agreed to publish Scriabin's work in 1894. This influential relationship led to an introduction to Tolstoy and then travel to Paris, where Scriabin mingled with the artistic demi-monde. Over the

Scriabin sought in his music to create the sensation of a transporting burst of energy, propelling the listener to ecstasy and divine transfiguration.

summer of 1899 he wrote the First Symphony; however, the first (incomplete) performance in St Petersburg was regarded as a failure, as was the follow-up (with choral finale) in Moscow in 1901. Having written a second at great speed in the summer of 1901, Scriabin soon started work on the third, 'The Divine Poem', which would occupy him until 1904. He wrote to a patroness, Margarita Morozov, that the performance would be 'the first proclamation of my new doctrine', more than hinting that music was not the only expression of his intellect and creativity. He read more philosophy and Greek myth and joined the Moscow Philosophical Society. During the summer of 1903 the Scriabins took a neighbouring dacha to the Pasternaks; Leonid Pasternak later made a drawing of the composer and, long after he had abandoned his ambition to compose, Pasternak's son Boris wrote a finely observed memoir of Scriabin.

Scandal surrounding his seduction of a teenage pupil provided Scriabin with a reason to leave Russia. He moved his wife and children to Switzerland in 1904, installing another mistress (Tatyana de Schloezer) in the next village. In Brussels he met the painter Delville (who later designed the cover for *Prometheus*) and other Theosophists to whom Scriabin felt able to propound his ideas. Homesickness eventually drove Scriabin and Tatyana back to Moscow in January 1909. His return was heralded by a concert which included the *The Poem of Ecstasy*: widespread critical acclaim, for so long denied to Scriabin in Russia, finally arrived.

From 1910 until his death Scriabin worked on ideas for the *Mysterium* and systemised the technical 'principles' by which he was to write his remaining music, the crystalline and technically unimpeachable piano works, unique in their luminosity. His recent critical successes were strengthened; reception to Scriabin was ecstatic in most quarters. Scriabin made his last public appearance in St Petersburg on 2 April 1915. Returning to Moscow, the first signs of blood poisoning were noticed. By the 11th crowds thronged the staircase of his flat. Scriabin died on 14 April, with the manuscript containing sketches for the *Mysterium* open on his piano. His funeral was said to have been the most fashionable event in Moscow for years.

Scriabin has long been regarded – some would say dismissed – as eccentric, even unhinged, for linking his music to a highly esoteric philosophy. This has caused his reputation as a composer to metamorphose repeatedly. He has been tarred by the Theosophist label (he read the teachings of the mystic and founder of Theosophy, Madame Helena Blavatsky) but, as he had done with others' music

and philosophies, he amalgamated doctrines which were consonant with his own temperament into his far more grandiose aims.

His attitudes and artistic goals were in fact shared by a number of his most brilliant contemporaries and, far from making him an outsider, they demonstrate that he was – unlike many of his fellow musicians – participating in some of the great cultural experiments of pre-Revolutionary Russia. The philosopher Vladimir Solovyov urged artists to reach beyond the notional confines of their activities, defining art as a process of 'materialisation of spirit and the spiritualisation of matter'. As interest has turned to the literary and artistic currents of the era of Symbolism in Russia (around 1890–1915), Scriabin's status is being reassessed. His ideas were highly influential in the artistic circles of early 20th-century Russia and ▷

LEFT
Madame Helena Blavatsky (1831–91), whose Theosophical teachings resonated with Scriabin's own thinking

RIGHT
The philosopher Vladimir Solovyov (1853–1900) urged artists to view their work in terms of a cross-transformation of spirit and matter

Amazons with Lions by Wassily Kandinsky (1866–1944): like Scriabin, Kandinsky was interested in the Theosophist teachings of Madame Blavatsky; Scriabin and Kandinsky both explored the connections between tones in music and in colour

had a decisive impact on the poet Alexander Blok, painter Wassily Kandinsky and particularly on Scriabin's friends, the poets Konstantin Balmont and Vyacheslav Ivanov. Scriabin sought in his music to create the sensation of a transporting burst of energy, propelling the listener to ecstasy and divine transfiguration. With his obsession with the mystical and his formulation of a ritualistic art form that would transport the participant – not merely the audience or performer (Solovyov had also emphasised the collective experience) – to a state of enlightenment, Scriabin in fact possessed a great deal in common with current artistic and philosophical thought.

Scriabin was emblematic of the visionary aspects of Russian Symbolism; he was regarded as a highly charismatic, legendary figure (due in part to his years abroad) and, as a composer of readily apparent originality, he was anointed figurehead of Russian modernism. Even if Scriabin's ego was massaged by adulation, he was often caustic about the music of his admirers. Stravinsky was infatuated with Scriabin's late work, but was rebuffed by the older composer, who found *Petrushka* 'very busy'. Scriabin's musical ideas were highly influential in early Soviet Russia, inspiring many composers – including Nikolay Myaskovsky, Nikolay Roslavets and Arthur Lourié – in their experimental work of that era. It has also been argued that the earthy, far-from-hedonistic

world of Shostakovich that dominated later Soviet music was in fact a reaction to Scriabin's otherworldly excesses.

Scriabin's augmentation of the orchestra with voices in the First Symphony was remarkable enough; by the time of *The Poem of Ecstasy* the forces are enormous, even in comparison with contemporary scores by Strauss and Schoenberg. However, despite the rate at which Scriabin's style developed, there is much consistency in the orchestral music. Take, for instance, the First Symphony and *The Poem of Ecstasy*: both pieces open with languorous clarinet melodies over a haze of shimmering strings (as does the earlier *Rêverie*) and both alternate this type of writing with the vigorous, rhythmically driven music also found in 'Luttes' ('Struggles'), the second movement of the Third Symphony, 'The Divine Poem'. All end in shatteringly joyous apotheoses.

Scriabin's piano compositions have inspired the greatest of pianists – including Ashkenazy, Gilels, Horowitz, Ogdon, Richter and Sofronitsky – to give some of their most noteworthy performances; viewed together, his 10 sonatas are arguably the most remarkable statements in the genre after Beethoven. As an innovator Scriabin avoided the pitfalls of many other modernists: when Schoenberg abandoned traditional harmonies, the result was dissonance and alienation of audiences; when Scriabin did the same by developing schemes for the manipulation of heady, brightly hued harmonies, he opened up huge, previously unheard vistas of sensual sound. ●

Jonathan Powell is a pianist, composer and writer with a particular interest in Russian music of the turn of the 20th century. He has performed the complete cycle of Scriabin's piano sonatas in several countries, and he contributed the article on the composer to the *New Grove Dictionary of Music and Musicians*.

Scriabin at the piano, with conductor Serge Koussevitzky: painting by Robert Sterl (1867–1932)

SCRIABIN AT THE PROMS

Piano Concerto in F sharp minor
Prom 9, 23 July

The Poem of Ecstasy (Symphony No. 4) Prom 46, 20 August

Rêverie Prom 40, 15 August

Symphony No. 1 in E major
Prom 41, 16 August

Symphony No. 3 in C major, 'The Divine Poem' Prom 52, 24 August

BBC

SCOTTISH SYMPHONY
ORCHESTRA

Donald Runnicles Chief Conductor
Ilan Volkov Principal Guest Conductor
Andrew Manze Associate Guest Conductor
Matthias Pintscher Artist in Association
Elizabeth Layton Leader

BBC PROMS SEASON INCLUDES
Donald Runnicles conducts Mahler's Symphony No.3, Nicola Benedetti plays Vaughan Williams' *The Lark Ascending*. Martyn Brabbins conducts Rimsky-Korsakov's *Scheherazade*, Ilan Volkov conducts Cage, Cardew and Feldman.

EDINBURGH INTERNATIONAL FESTIVAL 2010
Donald Runnicles conducts Mahler's Symphony No.8, Midori plays Bernstein's *Serenade*.
John Adams *El Niño*, featuring Willard White and Kelley O'Connor.

75TH BIRTHDAY SEASON 2010/11
Donald Runnicles conducts Brahms' *Ein Deutsches Requiem*. Ilan Volkov conducts Bruckner's Symphony No.5, Andrew Manze conducts Brahms' Symphony No.4, and Matthias Pintscher conducts Stravinsky's *Pulcinella*. Guest artists include Karen Cargill, Janine Jansen, Håkan Hardenberger and Steven Osborne.

New
Music

In a season that celebrates Henry Wood's contribution to the Proms and his support of the music of his day, we continue to build on his legacy of 'novelties', with 31 commissions and premieres. Robert Worby reveals a strong line-up of current British talent, and a range of composers spanning from Experimentalists Cornelius Cardew and Morton Feldman to a clutch of Scandinavians, including Hans Abrahamsen, Rued Langgaard and Bent Sørensen

Robert Worby is a composer, writer and broadcaster and is a regular presenter of Radio 3's *Hear and Now*.

Hans Abrahamsen
(born 1952)

Wald
BBC co-commission with Asko|Schönberg: UK premiere

Prom 28 6 August

Born in Denmark in 1952, Hans Abrahamsen studied with Per Nørgård and György Ligeti, among others. He has written many large ensemble works, including *Four Pieces for Orchestra*, which had its UK premiere at the Proms in 2005.

Wald is a series of variations based on the beginning of the composer's wind quintet *Walden* (1978), inspired by Henry David Thoreau's book of the same title, which describes a life of simplicity living in a log cabin near Walden Pond in Massachusetts. The composer says, 'I tried to search for the same simplicity, handling the most simple material, but at the same time trying not to lose the poetry.' The new piece maintains these ideas. It begins with a rising horn call (the composer is a horn player), with responses from other instruments, but these calls and responses occur at different speeds, causing their pattern to change and tumble throughout the piece.

Julian Anderson
(born 1967)

Fantasias
London premiere

Prom 29 7 August

Since 2007 Julian Anderson has been Composer-in-Residence and Professor of Composition at the Guildhall School of Music & Drama. Before that he taught at Harvard University for two years and at the Royal College of Music. Often influenced by folk music, he also employs bold orchestration that creates a richly sonorous experience for the listener.

Fantasias was given its premiere in the USA by the Cleveland Orchestra conducted by Jonathan Nott in November last year. This will be its London premiere after several performances in the UK. The work is in five contrasting movements with some unusual and varied scoring. The first movement, for example, uses only brass. The third employs static string and wind textures until a final eruption of orchestral colour at the end. The fourth movement is a *Tom and Jerry*-like scherzo, chopping around different instrumental groups. Anderson describes the final movement as 'a headlong rush, roller-coaster-like, as the music hurtles on its way'.

George Benjamin
(born 1960)

Duet
London premiere

Prom 22 2 August

This year marks George Benjamin's 50th birthday. At 16 he began studying with Messiaen and four years later his orchestral work *Ringed by the Flat Horizon* was performed at the Proms. His works have been performed by many of the world's leading orchestras and ensembles and in recent years there have been major retrospectives of his music in Berlin, Brussels, Madrid, Paris, Strasbourg and Tokyo. Benjamin has had close links with IRCAM, the centre for research into music, acoustics and technology founded in Paris by Pierre Boulez, and this has helped to shape his approach to composition.

Duet for piano and orchestra focuses on the sonic properties of the piano, the way its timbre changes across the keyboard, the ways notes decay and the simple fact that it can play chords. These characteristics are picked up by the orchestra – without violins – and they form the building blocks of textures through which the solo piano moves on its own independent path.

Cornelius Cardew
(1936–81)

Bun No. 1
London premiere

Prom 47 20 August

Cornelius Cardew was a seminal figure in the international Experimental music scene in the 1960s and 1970s. He studied and worked with Stockhausen and was later greatly influenced by Cage and other American Experimentalists. Along with Howard Skempton and Michael Parsons, Cardew founded the Scratch Orchestra in 1969. From the early 1970s his work became increasingly political and he composed music that attempted to 'draw the attention of listeners to social issues'.

Bun No. 1 for orchestra was composed and premiered in Rome in 1965. The piece is rarely heard – Cardew's orchestral works tend to be overlooked. Alvin Curran, a fellow composer who helped copy the parts for the premiere, recalls that it was 'notated conventionally in shockingly straight 4/4 or 3/4 time and was very melodic'. Cardew himself said enigmatically, 'This bun is a stone bun in milk.' He told his biographer, pianist John Tilbury, that, like a bun, the work was filling, but not substantial.

Tansy Davies
(born 1973)

Wild Card
BBC commission: world premiere

Prom 72 8 September

'Behind these sounds,' says Tansy Davies, 'lies the Fool's Journey – a journey through the Tarot cards – a metaphor for the journey through life.' Big themes but handled with a deft touch. *Wild Card* is linked to Davies's chamber piece *Falling Angel*, premiered by the Birmingham Contemporary Music Group in 2007. She goes on to say that, in the new piece, 'you'll hear flutterings – perhaps those of angels' wings – sometimes distant, sometimes up close, sometimes offset by macho brass. Bass and percussion work up some twisted funk, while the general mood remains decidedly ambiguous.' This is not unusual in Davies's work, where the Baroque may be contorted through clockwork techno or the medieval through raucous jazz. There's a touch of Stravinsky here, perhaps routed via the strident, street-band sound of Louis Andriessen, but Davies is very much a modern English composer, as her connections with the Aldeburgh Festival, the London Sinfonietta and the BCMG testify.

Brett Dean
(born 1961)

Amphitheatre
London premiere

Prom 18 30 July

Brett Dean describes *Amphitheatre* as 'a dramatic scene for large orchestra'. In one slow movement the piece describes a ruined Roman amphitheatre on the edge of a modern city. The composer took this scene from the opening of the children's book *Momo* by the German author Michael Ende. Dean takes the idea of the huge blocks of stone used in the construction of amphitheatres as a metaphorical building block for his piece. An oscillating brass chord, heard in the opening, is the foundation on which the work's structure is built. Using changing instrumental colour and distant trumpeting fanfares, *Amphitheatre* builds a picture of a noble public building and hints at past glories witnessed there.

Born in 1961 in Australia, Brett Dean studied in Brisbane before moving in 1984 to Germany, where he played viola in the Berlin Philharmonic Orchestra. He began composing there in 1988 and eventually returned to Australia to pursue composition.

James Dillon
(born 1950)

La navette
UK premiere

Prom 45 19 August

Glaswegian James Dillon is a self-taught composer (although he has studied art and design, linguistics and mathematics, and worked as a lab technician at Imperial College in the search for sub-atomic particles). During the 1980s he was grouped with a number of other British composers under the label 'New Complexists', so called because their notation was very detailed and, at the time, considered almost impossible to perform. This tag was rejected by all of the composers concerned. Notwithstanding their technical challenge, these works are now regularly performed as part of the contemporary music repertoire.

La navette was commissioned by the German radio station SWR and premiered at the Donaueschingen Musiktage in 2001. The piece is in one movement and has a rich, sumptuous surface comprising strings and high woodwinds, stretched across a sturdy brass-and-percussion framework. Overlapping rhythmic figures drive the piece towards a multi-layered conclusion.

Andy Potts (illustration, p.52); Line Harden (Abrahamsen, p.52); Maurice Foxall/Faber Music (Anderson, p.52); Maurice Foxall/Faber Music (Benjamin & Davies); Hulton Deutsch Collection/Corbis (Cardew); Mark Coulsen (Dean); Dylan Collard (Dillon)

Jonathan Dove
(born 1959)

A Song of Joys
BBC commission: world premiere

Prom 76 11 September

This new piece by Jonathan Dove is a special commission to open the Last Night of the Proms. It is a setting, for double chorus and orchestra, of a poem of the same title by Walt Whitman. The poem begins, 'O to make the most jubilant song! Full of music – full of manhood, womanhood, infancy!' It is a glorious celebration of music and befitting of the occasion.

Jonathan Dove is well known as a composer of opera and choral music as well as instrumental music. He has written over a dozen operas, including one for television about the death of Princess Diana, *When She Died*, which was broadcast in 2002 to around one million viewers in the UK alone. Reviewers often reflect on his contemporary use of tonality and conventional musical language. The composer himself comments, 'I found, to some extent, that restricting the palette seemed to give me greater freedom – I could be more expressive using fewer notes.' Of this new piece, he says, 'It will be festive!'

Morton Feldman
(1926–87)

Piano and Orchestra
London premiere

Prom 47 20 August

Morton Feldman was one of the composers who defined the New York school of Experimental music in the 1950s and 1960s. He was very much a New Yorker. Born in Brooklyn, he studied with Stefan Wolpe and was later greatly encouraged by John Cage. Almost all of his music is quiet and slow, composed intuitively without resort to any of the systems used by other composers in the mid-20th century. Towards the end of his life he began to compose very long works, one of which – a string quartet – lasts over six hours.

Piano and Orchestra, composed in 1975, is around 20 minutes in length and presents exquisite blocks of sounds that float in space akin to the way misty slabs of colour float in the paintings of Mark Rothko, an artist the composer greatly admired. Feldman was a master of instrumental register and this is particularly apparent in this piece, where 'sourceless' sounds, as he referred to them, suspend time in muted stillness.

Brian Ferneyhough
(born 1943)

Dum transisset I–IV
London premiere

Proms Saturday Matinee 5
4 September

Brian Ferneyhough's four movements for string quartet, *Dum transisset I–IV*, was commissioned by the Salzburg Festival and composed in 2006. It is based on a series of polyphonic compositions for viol consort written by the Renaissance composer Christopher Tye. But very little, if anything, of that sound-world survives in Ferneyhough's piece because, as he writes discursively, 'the work fades into a slightly perplexed and anxious attempt to repropose Tye materials as the remedy for the onset of chaos'.

Ferneyhough was born in Coventry 1943. He studied at the Birmingham School of Music and at the Royal Academy of Music, where one of his teachers was Lennox Berkeley. His music places formidable demands on players because his notation is painstakingly detailed and the works require great technical skill in performance. Ferneyhough's work draws on a wide range of references, including philosophy, literature, painting, mysticism and alchemy.

Alissa Firsova
(born 1986)

Bach Allegro
BBC commission: world premiere

Prom 39 14 August

Alissa Firsova was born in Moscow, in 1986, into a very musical family – both her parents are composers. When the family came to Britain in 1991, she studied at the Purcell School and then at the Royal Academy of Music, where she specialised in piano, conducting and composition. In 2001 she won the BBC Proms/*Guardian* Young Composer Competition with her piano piece *Les pavots*. Firsova is in great demand internationally as a pianist and she performed in Stravinsky's *Les noces* at the Proms last year.

Firsova's *Bach Allegro* is based on the third movement of Bach's Viola da gamba Sonata No. 3 in G minor, BWV 1029. She says she intends to 'Firsova-ise' it completely, although 'it's also important to keep a good balance with respect to the composer'. She cites the Schoenberg and Webern orchestrations of Bach as inspiring her most, and says 'the idea of this piece is to be contrasting – lively, colourful, fast and effective!'

Graham Fitkin
(born 1963)

PK
BBC commission: world premiere

Prom 60 30 August

Graham Fitkin is known for his hard-edged rhythmic scores that are usually unashamedly tonal but often complex. He was born in 1963 in West Cornwall, where he is still based, having studied at the University of Nottingham and with Louis Andriessen in Amsterdam. His new work, *PK*, for the BBC Concert Orchestra and this year's Cornwall- and London-based Proms Family Orchestra, emphasises his Cornish connections.

In 1870 the UK was linked up to India and subsequently the USA by a chain of telegraphic cables which came ashore at Porthcurno in West Cornwall. PK is the telegraphic code name for Porthcurno. This tiny village was once the world's largest cable station, with 14 telegraphic cable links in operation (the company that laid the cables later merged into Cable & Wireless). Fitkin says, 'I am interested in how a small village at a remote end of England became a key part of the country's communications system. The new piece will work through signals, switches and flow of current.'

Robin Holloway
(born 1943)

RELIQUARY
BBC commission:
world premiere

`Prom 74  9 September`

Robin Holloway began his career by embracing modernism but later engaged with Romanticism, a transition seen not least in his affection for the music of Schumann. *RELIQUARY* (subtitled 'Scenes from the life of Mary, Queen of Scots, enclosing an instrumentation of Schumann's *Gedichte der Königin Maria Stuart*) is not a straightforward orchestration of Schumann's song-cycle. Rather, Holloway has chosen to embellish the work with a prologue, interludes and an epilogue. 'If the songs are the jewels,' he says, 'I have provided the setting.' He has done so with empathy and sympathy. Schumann wrote this music when he was a sick man and the poems were written when Mary, Queens of Scots, was incarcerated by her cousin Elizabeth I. Holloway speaks of 'opening up the claustrophobia' experienced by Mary in her physical prison and by Schumann in the confinement of his sickness. He has extended Schumann's work, intensified the focus on Mary and made us more aware of her plight.

Simon Holt
(born 1958)

a table of noises
London premiere

`Prom 13  26 July`

Simon Holt's percussion concerto, written for Colin Currie, was premiered in 2008 by the City of Birmingham Symphony Orchestra under Martyn Brabbins. The percussion part is scored for a collection of instruments arranged on a tabletop – hence the title – where the performer is seated. This idea was inspired in part by the composer's great-uncle Ash, a disabled taxidermist who kept all the tools of his trade close to hand on a table.

The work is in six sections with titles that refer to Ash's trade – 'a drawer full of eyes', 'under glass', 'jute'. The orchestra includes nine non-standard woodwind that occupy extremes of pitch, 10 brass, two orchestral percussionists, harp, celesta and strings without violins. Unusual instrumental groupings provide rich textures that sometimes support the solo part and are sometimes set against it. Markings in the score such as 'meccanico' and 'like a brittle and neurotic machine' indicate curious, offbeat rhythms.

Gabriel Jackson
(born 1962)

In nomine Domini
BBC commission:
world premiere

`Proms Saturday Matinee 5`
4 September

Gabriel Jackson was a chorister at Canterbury Cathedral before studying composition at the Royal College of Music. His music is performed internationally and, here in the UK, has been heard at major festivals, including those of Huddersfield, Aldeburgh and Cheltenham. Last year he became Associate Composer of the BBC Singers, who have been performing his music for over a decade.

In nomine Domini, written for the BBC Singers, includes harp and percussion and four 'In nomine' interpolations for string quartet. The text is a poem by the murdered missionary John Bradburne, from which the piece takes its name, and was chosen partly because it fitted the composer's concept for the piece. 'I am quite intrigued by the poem's provenance,' says Jackson, 'and also the fact that its meaning is not terribly clear.' He has declared that his works are not about conflict and resolution. 'Even when animated, they are essentially contemplative. I like repetition and ritualised structures.'

Jouni Kaipainen
(born 1956)

String Quartet No. 6
BBC co-commission with Royal Philharmonic Society: world premiere

`Proms Chamber Music 2`
26 July

Jouni Kaipainen was born in Helsinki in 1956 and studied at the Sibelius Academy. In the 1970s he was an active member of the Ears Open society – a group of composers who were considered a fortress of Finnish modernism well into the 1980s. Kaipainen fitted well into that mould at the time, but since those days both he and the society have engaged with a more pluralistic approach to composition. His roots go back to a kind of Expressionism that might be associated with Berg but, having worked through a strident period of post-Serialism, his musical language is now more muted and restrained, with a focus on lucidity and coherence.

Kaipainen has written many works for a wide variety of forces, including choral music, songs, symphonies, music for keyboard and chamber music. The string quartets are a very important part of his output and reflect a clarity found in his recent work that comes from this Classical instrumental grouping.

Rued Langgaard
(1893–1952)

Music of the Spheres
UK premiere

`Prom 35  11 August`

Langgaard's parents were musicians in the Danish royal household and he began his musical life aged 5, progressing quickly using his natural gifts. He was a prolific composer, writing over 400 works, including 16 symphonies, choral pieces, songs, string quartets and an opera. Unfortunately his compositional career was not a great success but since his death there has been a revival of interest in his work, borne out by many performances and recordings.

Music of the Spheres is a large-scale work for soloist, choir, organ, orchestra and 'distant' orchestra. It was completed in 1918 when Langgaard was in his mid-twenties. It comprises 15 short sections, each with enticing, perhaps eccentric, titles – 'Like Sunbeams on a Coffin Decorated with Sweet-Smelling Flowers', 'Chaos – Ruin – Far and Near', 'Bells Pealing: Look! He Comes'. The work is lavish with sumptuous sonorities and grand gestures. It sounds surprisingly modern, utilising repetition, spatial effects and static rhythms.

James MacMillan
(born 1959)

**The Sacrifice –
Three Interludes**
London premiere

Prom 69 6 September

James MacMillan took these three interludes from his 2007 opera *The Sacrifice* to form a symphonic suite which was premiered by the BBC Philharmonic, conducted by the composer, in Manchester in 2008. Their function in the opera is to provide periods of reflection, creating a breathing space giving time for consideration and deliberation. The opera's narrative draws on *The Mabinogion*, a collection of ancient Welsh folk tales, and tells of a ruler's sacrifices to secure the future of his divided country, weaving age-old themes of love, jealousy, revenge and war into a tense web. The interludes reflect this intensity, maintaining a sense of drama using strident brass and energetic strings punctuated by fervent percussion.

Celtic themes infuse much of MacMillian's work. Born in Scotland in 1959, he celebrates his Scottish roots, his Catholic faith and his socialist politics, all of which provide a robust underpinning to his musical life. He is also a well-established conductor.

Martin Matalon
(born 1958)

Lignes de fuite
UK premiere

Prom 63 2 September

Martin Matalon was born in Buenos Aires in 1958. He studied in Boston and then at the Juilliard School of Music. He moved to Paris in 1993 and began a fruitful collaboration with IRCAM, the high-tech research centre for music and acoustics founded in Paris by Pierre Boulez. Matalon's works include a large number of compositions with live electronics and new scores for several classic films by the Surrealist film director Luis Buñuel.

Composed in 2007, *Lignes de fuite* ('Lines of Flight') is an orchestral work with four connecting movements. The title relates to an idea from drawing and painting, where lines are added to an image to produce depth or perspective. The lines in this work can be heard as changes of timbre, pitch, register, texture and melodic ideas that thread through the movements, connecting them as one builds on another. But there is a built-in instability within the large-scale structure and the music flashes from one idea to another, creating variation and contrast.

Colin Matthews
(born 1946)

Violin Concerto
London premiere

Prom 15 28 July

Colin Matthews's Violin Concerto was premiered last September by Leila Josefowicz and the City of Birmingham Symphony Orchestra under Oliver Knussen. It was extremely well received by the critics: 'strikingly original work,' said *The Guardian*, while *The Sunday Times* reported 'a wealth of savourable orchestral detail'. The violin part is virtuosic throughout but there is no cadenza, no place where virtuosity takes centre stage. 'There is no unnecessary flashiness here,' says Matthews, 'and the concerto is not designed as a showpiece.' Nonetheless, this two-movement work presents a glorious display of orchestral colour and dazzling writing for the violin.

Colin Matthews is well established in the contemporary music world. He worked with Benjamin Britten and Imogen Holst at Aldeburgh and with Deryck Cooke on the performing version of Mahler's 10th Symphony. His music is performed throughout the world and has been recorded extensively.

David Matthews (born 1943) /
Vaughan Williams (1872–1958)

Dark Pastoral
*BBC commission:
world premiere*

Prom 67 5 September

Dark Pastoral is based on the surviving fragment of the slow movement of Vaughan Williams's Cello Concerto (1942). The unfinished concerto was to have been performed by Pablo Casals and the original manuscript is now in the British Library. The first movement, entitled 'Rhapsody', is complete in short score. The final movement was difficult to decipher, not least because Vaughan Williams's handwriting is notoriously poor. Matthews was drawn to the second movement because it had the most potential. The first section of this new piece is as Vaughan Williams composed it; the second section is pure Matthews; and the third section is a development by Matthews of the first section. The harmonic language and the feeling of an English tradition relate to the fabric of both composers. Matthews likens the experience of writing this work to putting on Vaughan Williams's coat – it's not his but it fits and he can walk out in it.

Stephen Montague
(born 1943)

Wilful Chants
*BBC commission:
world premiere*

Prom 30 8 August

American Stephen Montague has been based in London since the mid-1970s. Among his musical heroes are Charles Ives, Henry Cowell and John Cage, and his work is infused with an American pioneering spirit. His Concerto for piano and orchestra was premiered at the Proms in 1997 and, like the music of Ives, it draws on well-known American hymn tunes, spirituals and folk songs.

Wilful Chants is a work for chorus, brass and percussion that places the sound of language at its core. Using a variety of texts and pan-world sources, including nonsense words and phrases, the piece celebrates the character of human utterance. Extended vocal techniques draw the listener deep into the sounds of speech and beyond, towards a musical world full of rhythm, vitality and exuberance. A familiar fast–slow–fast structure, leading to an exhilarating conclusion, provides a solid musical framework for an extraordinary and engaging sound-world.

Thea Musgrave
(born 1928)

Ithaca
*BBC commission:
world premiere*

Proms Saturday Matinee 5
4 September

Ithaca is a setting of a poem written in 1911 by the Greek poet C. P. Cavafy (1863–1933), relating to Odysseus's return to Ithaca (as told in Homer's *Odyssey*), the nature of his journey and experiences encountered on the way – some potentially perilous, some delightful. The poet stresses that it is the journey that is important rather than the destination, creating a metaphor for our journey through life.

'Choosing the text is an exciting and crucial decision,' says Scottish-American composer Musgrave. 'When my eyes fell on *Ithaca* I thought, "Aha, this is the one!"' She has worked with singers for many years and tries to use words as expressively as possible. For her, harmony is a balance between the horizontal – the passage of time – and what she calls 'the perpendicular' – notes sounding together. The connections between Musgrave's concept of harmony and the expressiveness of text underpin the piece, the score of which is marked 'Ecstatic'.

Betty Olivero
(born 1954)

Neharot, Neharot
UK premiere

Proms Saturday Matinee 3
21 August

Betty Olivero is an Israeli composer who, having spent much of her career in Florence, has now returned to her home country. Her music draws on traditional, ethnic material that is recomposed using contemporary techniques. Often the transformations she employs are so extensive that the original forms are unrecognisable, yet, as she says, 'their spirit and highly charged dramatic potential remain untouched'.

Neharot, Neharot ('Rivers, Rivers') refers to the rivers of tears shed by women in disastrous situations. The work is scored for viola, accordion, percussion, two string orchestras and tape and is a response to the horrors of war, experienced by both sides, during the conflict between Israel and Hezbollah in Lebanon in 2006. Recordings of women in mourning, along with elegies and love songs from the Middle East and Africa, surface during the piece, in which the solo viola and the orchestra are used as a metaphor for the relationship between an individual and the society to which they belong.

Tarik O'Regan
(born 1978)

Latent Manifest
*BBC commission:
world premiere*

Prom 39 14 August

Tarik O'Regan's new orchestral work, *Latent Manifest*, takes as its starting point the first movement of Bach's Sonata No. 3 in C major for solo violin, BWV 1005. O'Regan is fascinated by the way a single line of music can suggest bigger textures and elements of four-part polyphony so, as composers have done throughout history, he has spent a great deal of time studying music from the past to discover how it works. He suggests that his methods of analysis are 'rather like a student of film today looking back at the classics. Perhaps he or she might stop the reel frame by frame and, in doing so, not only uncover special effects but also begin to think about a new language of their own.' The title of the new piece refers to O'Regan's response to the manifestation of 'hidden' musical lines in the original.

O'Regan studied at Oxford and Cambridge universities. He currently works at Princeton, where he is composing an opera based on Joseph Conrad's *Heart of Darkness*.

Arvo Pärt
(born 1935)

Symphony No. 4, 'Los Angeles'
UK premiere

Prom 46 20 August

Arvo Pärt is known as a master of profound small-scale works; a craftsman of contemplative miniatures evoking 'tintinnabulation' – the almost sacred, resonant decay of bells. His music stems from a deep-seated spirituality that was nourished by his study of medieval music. He has not written a symphony in nearly four decades and this new large-scale work was greeted with great surprise and astonishment, not least because the conductor Esa-Pekka Salonen, who commissioned the piece, was expecting a short 'prayer' for orchestra. When the piece arrived, the 'prayer' was there but it formed the central movement of this three-movement symphony. Salonen gave the premiere with the Los Angeles Philharmonic last year.

The work is dedicated to the jailed Russian oligarch Mikhail Khodorkovsky. 'With my composition,' writes Pärt, 'I would like to reach out my hand, extending it to the prisoner, and in his person to all those imprisoned without rights in Russia.'

Albert Schnelzer
(born 1972)

A Freak in Burbank
UK premiere

Prom 51 23 August

Albert Schnelzer studied at the Malmö Academy of Music and London's Royal College of Music, and is one of Sweden's most performed contemporary composers. He has written orchestral pieces, concertos and a wide range of chamber music that has been performed throughout the world. 'For me,' he says, 'there are basically two primary activities in human music history: dancing and singing. Therefore, I have worked intensively with developing somewhat neglected elements such as pulse, metre and melody.'

A Freak in Burbank was inspired by the music of Haydn and the work of the film director Tim Burton, born in Burbank, California. Schnelzer says that transparency, playful character, contrasts and an almost burlesque quality are common to both. He's attempted to put a Haydn-sized orchestra in a modern environment. Although Haydn was the initial inspiration, Burton took over during the writing of the piece, which is bright with great attention to detail.

energyrethinking
use less
save more

Be **instrumental** in rethinking
how to use energy in a better way

energyrethinking.org is a community where we help each other to be smarter about how we use energy.

This means rethinking how we can use energy differently to save money and do our bit for the environment by sharing tips, advice and ideas.

Start rethinking now at

www.energyrethinking.org

at home

travel and transport

at work

lifestyle and leisure

In association with

Gunther Schuller
(born 1925)

Where the Word Ends
UK premiere

Prom 5 20 July

It was Gunther Schuller who, in 1957, coined the phrase 'Third Stream', referring to a confluence where jazz and classical music meet. As a young man he played the horn in orchestras conducted by Toscanini and in jazz bands directed by Miles Davis and Gil Evans. He went on to have great influence as a teacher at Yale, Tanglewood and the Manhattan School of Music and has composed over 180 works.

Where the Word Ends was premiered in February last year by the Boston Symphony Orchestra and James Levine. It is a large-scale, symphony-like orchestral work in a single movement. The opening *Lento* establishes the harmonic and textural world of the whole piece. This is followed by three other sections with a Scherzo, complete with a Trio, disrupting the second *Adagio* section. After this shift, the easy pace returns until strong rhythms and big punctuating chords drive the final *Allegro vivace* section to an exuberant conclusion.

Bent Sørensen
(born 1958)

La mattina
UK premiere

Prom 53 25 August

Danish composer Bent Sørensen describes *La mattina*, his second piano concerto, as the 'darkest and most profound work I have ever written'. But it began breezily with Sørensen and the pianist Leif Ove Andsnes relaxing with a glass of wine in a piano bar in Vienna. Andsnes seated himself at the piano and played Busoni's transcription of Bach's organ work *Ich ruf' zu dir, Herr Jesu Christ*. Sørensen says, 'I could see his hands playing something from the abyss that floats upwards and in the end becomes a halo over our heads.' He returned home, began work and the piano concerto *La mattina* was born. It was premiered last year in Oslo by Andsnes and the Norwegian Chamber Orchestra.

Sørensen studied with Per Nørgård at the Jutland Music Academy. His unique sound-world is achieved by blurring conventional harmony with microtonal inflections and tiny glissandos. Composer Arne Nordheim declares, 'It reminds me of something I've never heard.'

Mark-Anthony Turnage
(born 1960)

Hammered Out
BBC co-commission with Los Angeles Philharmonic: world premiere

Prom 54 26 August

The title of this new piece by Turnage will come as no surprise to those who know his work. Titles such as *Blood on the Floor*, *Three Screaming Popes* and *Scorched* reveal a composer confronting life head on. But, conversely, *Quiet Life*, *A Soothing Interlude* and *Cradle Song* tell another story. Turnage inhabits both musical worlds but, now aged 50, he's said of this new work, 'I don't want to write an old man's piece', indicating that we should expect something bold and extrovert. Jazz, funk and other popular forms inform his musical thinking even though he's firmly rooted in the classical tradition.

Turnage has received many prizes and accolades and has undertaken residencies and associations with major institutions, including the BBC, City of Birmingham and Chicago Symphony orchestras, the London Philharmonic Orchestra, English National Opera and the Royal College of Music. But these connections have never confined his work in any way and he is often still thought of as a controversial radical.

Huw Watkins
(born 1976)

Violin Concerto
BBC commission: world premiere

Prom 42 17 August

'I'm playing with expectations,' says Huw Watkins. 'This is a concerto in three movements but it isn't necessarily fast–slow–fast or solo with accompaniment. Although the violin is leading the orchestra and carries the musical argument, the orchestra amplifies the musical ideas but also interrupts them.' Watkins has previously written *Partita* for violinist Alina Ibragimova in 2006, and he's greatly impressed by her technical skill. His Violin Concerto presents her with some serious technical challenges and he describes the first movement particularly as 'obsessive and fiendish'. The work is built on musical cells which are linked, extended and developed and, although the orchestra is not large, Watkins teases out some rich, dark textures through astute use of register and dynamics.

As well as being a composer, Watkins is in great demand as a pianist, in which role he appears alongside musicians from the Royal College of Music in the Composer Portrait preceding his Prom.

Composer Portraits

This season's Composer Portraits offer the chance to hear chamber music by Tansy Davies, James Dillon, Colin Matthews and Huw Watkins, before premieres of their works at the Royal Albert Hall later the same evening. As well as featuring performances by musicians from some of the leading British conservatories, the series features each composer in conversation.

Tansy Davies
8 September, 5.15pm

grind show (electric)
salt box
neon
Musicians from the Guildhall School of Music & Drama

James Dillon
19 August, 5.45pm

Zone (… de azul)
Charm
dragonfly
… Once Upon a Time
Royal Scottish Academy MusicLab

Colin Matthews
28 July, 5.45pm

Chaconne with Chorale and Moto perpetuo
Scorrevole
Calmo
Duo No. 3
Enigma No. 1
Britten, arr. Colin Matthews **Sonnet**
Musicians from the Royal Academy of Music

Huw Watkins
17 August, 5.15pm

Gig
Four Inventions
Sad Steps
Huw Watkins *piano*
Musicians from the Royal College of Music

Welsh National *Opera* Cenedlaethol Cymru

Great performances of great operas

Autumn 2010

NEW PRODUCTION
Fidelio
B e e t h o v e n
Supported by the Friends of WNO

The Magic Flute
M o z a r t

Ariadne auf Naxos
R i c h a r d   S t r a u s s

See us in Cardiff, Swansea, Bristol, Liverpool, Birmingham, Llandudno, Southampton and Oxford

Spring 2011

NEW PRODUCTION
Die Fledermaus
J o h a n n   S t r a u s s   II
Supported by the WNO *Partnership*

Il trovatore
V e r d i
Supported by the WNO Idloes Owen Society

See us in Cardiff, Birmingham, Llandudno, Southampton, Bristol, Plymouth and Milton Keynes

Summer 2011

NEW PRODUCTION
Così fan tutte
M o z a r t
Sponsored by Associated British Ports

Turandot
P u c c i n i
Sponsored by WNO Sponsors' Group

See us in Cardiff and Birmingham

Join WNO's free mailing list
0800 328 2357
marketing@wno.org.uk
wno.org.uk

Registered Charity No 221538. *Ariadne auf Naxos* (2004 cast pictured) photo by Clive Barda

Supported by
 **The National Lottery**
through the Arts Council of Wales

 Cyngor Celfyddydau Cymru
Arts Council of Wales

 Noddir gan
Lywodraeth Cynulliad Cymru
Sponsored by
Welsh Assembly Government

 Supported by
ARTS COUNCIL ENGLAND

 City of London Festival

Discover the Festival . . . enjoy the City
21 JUNE – 9 JULY

3 concerts in St Paul's Cathedral

- Monteverdi: Vespers (1610) with the Choir of St Paul's Cathedral, conducted by Andrew Carwood
- Haydn: The Creation with the OAE, Philharmonic Chorus, conducted by Thierry Fischer
- Beethoven: Symphony No 9 with the LSO, the Monteverdi Choir, conducted by Sir John Eliot Gardiner

Early evening series in City churches, including 'Discoveries' from the BBC New Generation Artists

Music and arts of the Portuguese-speaking world

- Choral polyphony in beautiful churches
- Brazilian Capoeira at historic City landmarks
- Bach meets Villa Lobos and new works in lovely Livery halls
- Family Day on Hampstead Heath
- Fado, wine tasting and much more

Music and honey: Street Pianos and Urban Beehives throughout the Square Mile

www.colf.org

For the latest news and special offers join our Facebook fanpage at www.facebook.com   Follow us on Twitter: twitter.com/CoLFestival

GLYNDEBOURNE
ON TOUR 2010

MOZART
DON GIOVANNI
A new production from the 2010 Festival

ROSSINI
LA CENERENTOLA
A revival of Sir Peter Hall's 2005 Festival
production

MONTEVERDI
L'INCORONAZIONE
DI POPPEA
A revival of Robert Carsen's 2008 Festival
production

GLYNDEBOURNE	9–30 OCTOBER
WOKING	2–6 NOVEMBER
MILTON KEYNES	9–13 NOVEMBER
NORWICH	16–20 NOVEMBER
PLYMOUTH	23–27 NOVEMBER
STOKE-ON-TRENT	30 NOVEMBER – 4 DECEMBER

**To find out full details of the 2010 Tour
visit www.glyndebourne.com**

www.glyndebourne.com

The Tour is supported by  Supported by **ARTS COUNCIL ENGLAND**

FIRST KNIGHT
OF THE PROMS

During nearly 50 years at the helm of the Proms, founder-conductor Henry Wood transformed both the range of repertoire presented to audiences and the quality of his Queen's Hall Orchestra. As the BBC Proms honours him with a Henry Wood Day, Andrew Green profiles Britain's first great conductor

Workaholic. That was Henry Wood. When Queen's Hall manager Robert Newman invited the not-yet-established 25-year-old conductor to build on the existing London fashion for promenade concerts by directing a freshly conceived series at Queen's Hall in 1895, can he have realised his good fortune? In Wood he found someone prepared to devote himself body and soul to an insane workload that brought night after night of Promenade concerts with the Queen's Hall Orchestra, bulging with repertoire that could never be adequately rehearsed given the financial resources available.

And so to a second key Wood trait. Discipline. The word even forms a chapter title in Wood's autobiography, *My Life of Music* (1938). How did he cope with the challenge of conducting every one of the Queen's Hall 'Promenades' (never 'Proms' to Wood) plus the other concert series given by the Queen's Hall Orchestra? Simple. An obsession with preparation, not least when it came to marking individual orchestral parts (through the night if required) to save time in rehearsal.

And the personal discipline Wood embraced was demanded of his players. Morning rehearsals started

'Make the old ladies jump!' was one cry so familiar that players would call it out before he did.

at 10.00am, not a second later – a shock to the old hands of the orchestra. A player arriving late might receive the dreaded greeting, 'Another cab horse down?'. And there was no sneaking out for a furtive cigarette during a 197-bar rest.

Entirely self-taught as a conductor, Wood swiftly learnt to make the best use of rehearsal time, targeting key passages and yelling instructions over the music in those characteristic whining tones, rather than call a halt. 'Make the old ladies jump!' was one cry so familiar that players would call it out

before he did. In his biography of Wood, Reginald Pound recounts how, in delirium during a serious illness a year before his death in 1944, the conductor sat up in bed and drove his imagined players on in an imagined rehearsal. Old habits …

In the entertaining (if error-strewn) *My Life of Music*, Wood recounted the occasion when Ravel turned up at 10.00am to rehearse the orchestra in his own music, only to fritter away time cutting the orchestra down in size. Wood was beside himself. 'The first note they played was at 10.23 by my watch!'

However, there was plenty more to Wood than drive and discipline. The two Henry Wood Day concerts (5 September) at this year's BBC Proms make that abundantly clear. In the matinee event – a (slightly tweaked) recreation of the Last Night of the Proms from 100 years ago – his famous *Fantasia on British Sea-Songs* and, intriguingly, his orchestration of Musorgsky's *The Peep-Show* reflect Wood's early ambitions in composition.

In the evening concert – featuring works either dedicated to or otherwise associated with Wood – a rare outing for Dorothy Howell's *Lamia* points to the fact that Wood was 'gender blind' in musical terms. This short piece was hugely successful when introduced at the 1919 Proms. (Ethel Smyth was another composer to benefit from Wood's promotion, though that didn't stop her branding him 'weak, superficial and contemptible' when he deserted his second wife.) Wood also insisted female orchestral musicians should receive equal pay to men.

Above all, in the Henry Wood Day concerts – and in works scheduled throughout the season of which he gave the world or UK premieres –

HENRY WOOD DAY AT THE PROMS
Sunday 5 September

Prom 67, 2.30pm
FREE Prom
'Recreation' of the programme from the Last Night of the Proms 1910

Prom 68, 8.00pm
Programme of works dedicated to or associated with Henry Wood

The memorial window at St Sepulchre-without-Newgate, London, the 'Musicians' Church', where Wood was assistant organist and where his ashes are buried

we see Wood's passion for musical adventure and education. Over the decades this steadily moved the Proms away from its roots in the bits and pieces of crowd-pleasing musical miscellanies. Among foreign composers, the 5 September line-up features the likes of Wagner, Tchaikovsky, Sibelius – and Beethoven, seen by Wood as needing a leg-up with the wider public. Bartók, Mahler, Hindemith and a host of others benefited likewise. As for British composers featured on Henry Wood Day – such as Vaughan Williams, Elgar and Bax – Wood didn't just grant them exposure at home, he confidently scheduled their music on conducting trips abroad.

Wood's dedication to new music was never better demonstrated than in scheduling the world premiere of Schoenberg's *Five Orchestral Pieces* at a 1912 Promenade concert. Hisses, laughter and much puzzlement ensued. 'Stick to it, gentlemen!' Wood had yelled at rehearsal. 'This is nothing to what you'll have to play in 25 years' time!'

The Vaughan Williams connection on Henry Wood Day (the reworking by David Matthews of fragments from the unfinished Cello Concerto) stirs thoughts of perhaps the peak moment of Wood's career: his October 1938 Jubilee concert in the Royal Albert Hall, marking his 50 years as a conductor. Vaughan Williams's *Serenade to* ▶

BBC, Chris Christodoulou/BBC (p62); Malcolm Crowthers (above right)

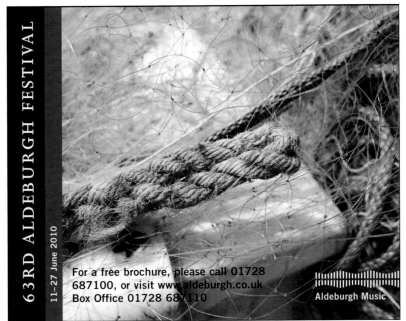

Showing his metal: Henry Wood in the workshop of his home in Ealing, London, 1935

Music was commissioned for the occasion and reduced to tears the star performer that night – Sergey Rachmaninov, one of the army of legends with whom Wood worked. (Rachmaninov's First Piano Concerto also features on Henry Wood Day.)

The first modern British conductor of serious note, with an appeal to advertisers that saw him endorsing cigarettes as well as gramophone records, Wood perhaps didn't enjoy quite the international career we might have expected, though things picked up late on. Did he really not receive the offers? OK, Wood's biographer Arthur Jacobs described him as 'the least literary or intellectual of conductors', but many who know Wood's recordings will feel this view to be ungenerous.

Certainly, the ties that bound Wood to the huge commitment of Newman's concerts (and always to the Proms, under subsequent management) were extraordinarily strong. In 1917, a full 22 years after he first directed the Queen's Hall Orchestra, Wood received the offer of a long guest-conducting stint with the Boston Symphony Orchestra. He was surely in no doubt as to how the prestigious nature of the engagement could further a career. After much hesitation – and emotional blackmail from Newman ('Don't you know there's a war on?') – Wood turned down the offer.

Yet, given Wood's utter devotion to the Proms (he conducted over 5,000), it's no overstatement to say that without him the concerts might not have survived. Their complete identification with Wood created a unique 'brand'. During the Second World War an Australian airman said he'd come to London to do two things: 'fly Spitfires and hear Sir Henry Wood'.

The burning-down of Queen's Hall during that war may have been a tragic and enduring loss to London's concert life, but one shred of consolation is that as a result we have a recording of Wood contributing with others to a broadcast memorialising this great venue in August 1941. The programme may sound a touch wooden, but it remains a charming memory of Wood's distinctive voice and ineffable enthusiasm. 'Would you live [the Proms] over again, Sir Henry?' he's asked. 'Every day and every hour,' comes the response. ●

Andrew Green is a broadcaster, writer and historian who contributes to many journals. His programme *Sir Henry's Hoard*, exploring Wood's vast collection of concert programmes, will be broadcast by BBC Radio 3 on 4 September.

A database of all Proms performances is currently being prepared and will be available via the Proms website later this year.

Hulton Archive/Getty Images/Royal College of Music

PERFORMANCES THIS SEASON OF WORKS GIVEN THEIR WORLD OR UK PREMIERES BY HENRY WOOD

Bach Brandenburg Concerto No. 1 (†1908)
Proms Saturday Matinee 1, 14 August

Bach, orch. Henry Wood 'Suite No. 6' –
Prelude; Finale (*1916) Prom 39, 14 August

Chabrier Joyeuse marche (†1896)
Prom 76, Saturday 11 September

Debussy Prélude à L'après-midi d'un faune
(†1904) Prom 71, 7 September

Dvořák, orch. Henry Wood Humoresque
G flat major, Op. 101 No. 7 (*1909)
Prom 67, 5 September

Elgar Pomp and Circumstance March No. 4
in G major (*1907) Prom 67, 5 September

Howell Lamia (*1919) Prom 68, 5 September

Janáček Taras Bulba (†1928) Prom 32, 9 August

Mahler Symphony No. 1 in D major (†1903)
Prom 65, 3 September

Mahler Symphony No. 4 (†1905)
Prom 26, 5 August

Mahler Symphony No. 7 (†1913)
Prom 34, 10 August

Mahler Symphony No. 8, 'Symphony
of a Thousand' (†1930) Prom 1, 16 July

Musorgsky, orch. Henry Wood
The Peep-Show (*1909) Prom 67, 5 September

Musorgsky, arr. Henry Wood Pictures at
an Exhibition (*1915) Prom 63, 2 September

Musorgsky, arr. Rimsky-Korsakov
A Night on the Bare Mountain (†1898)
Prom 40, 15 August

Prokofiev Piano Concerto No. 1 (†1920)
Prom 8, 22 July

Rachmaninov Piano Concerto No. 1 in
F sharp minor (†1900) Prom 68, 5 September

Ravel Piano Concerto for the Left Hand
(†1932) Prom 46, 20 August

Ravel Valses nobles et sentimentales (†1913)
Prom 22, 2 August

Ravel La valse (†1921) Prom 22, 2 August

Rimsky-Korsakov Sheherazade (†1896)
Prom 45, 19 August

Schoenberg Five Orchestral Pieces, Op. 16
(*1912) Prom 66, 4 September

Shostakovich Symphony No. 7 in C major,
'Leningrad' (†1942) Prom 8, 22 July

Sibelius Karelia Suite (†1906)
Prom 68, 5 September

Tchaikovsky Eugene Onegin – Waltz and
Polonaise (†1892) Prom 68, 5 September

Tchaikovsky Manfred (†1898) Prom 4, 19 July

Tchaikovsky Suite No. 3 in G major, Op. 55
(†1897) Prom 44, 18 August

Vaughan Williams Serenade to Music
(*1938) Prom 23, 3 August

Wood Fantasia on British Sea-Songs (*1905)
Prom 67, 5 September

* world premiere † UK premiere

London Philharmonic Orchestra

2010-2011 Season at Southbank Centre's Royal Festival Hall
Including 13 concerts to mark Mahler's anniversary year

BOOK NOW
London Philharmonic Orchestra Ticket Office
020 7840 4242 | www.lpo.org.uk
Mon-Fri 10am-5pm; no booking fee

Southbank Centre Ticket Office
0844 847 9920 Daily 9am-8pm; £2.50 booking fee
www.southbankcentre.co.uk £1.45 booking fee
In person at the Royal Festival Hall Ticket Office.
Daily 10am-8pm; no booking fee

Early season highlights include:

Wednesday 22 September 2010 | 7.30pm
Zemlinsky *Six Maeterlinck Songs, Op. 13*
Mahler *Symphony No. 3*

Vladimir Jurowski *conductor*
Petra Lang *mezzo soprano*
London Philharmonic Choir
Trinity Boys Choir

Saturday 25 September 2010 | 7.30pm
Haydn *Symphony No. 63 (La Roxelane)*
Matteo D'Amico *Flight from Byzantium*
(world premi re)
Dufay *Moribus et genere; Vergene bella*
Dufay *Lamentatio sanctae matris ecclesiae
Constantinopolitanae*
Bartók *The Miraculous Mandarin (complete)*

Vladimir Jurowski *conductor*
Hilliard Ensemble
London Philharmonic Choir

Wednesday 6 October 2010 | 7.30pm
Suk *Scherzo fantastique*
Chopin *Piano Concerto No. 2*
Dvořák *Symphony No. 9 (From the New World)*

Neeme Järvi *conductor*
Evgeny Kissin *piano*

Saturday 23 October 2010 | 7.00pm
Rossini *Aureliano in Palmira*

Maurizio Benini *conductor*
Annick Massis *Zenobia*
Silvia Tro Santafé *Arsace*
Kenneth Tarver *Aureliano*
Andrew Foster-Williams *Gran Sacerdote*
Ezgi Kutlu *Publia*
Geoffrey Mitchell Choir

Wednesday 27 October 2010 | 7.30pm
Mendelssohn *Symphony No. 5 (Reformation)*
Mahler *Kindertotenlieder*
Brahms *Symphony No. 3*

Vladimir Jurowski *conductor*
Sarah Connolly *mezzo soprano*

Saturday 30 October 2010 | 7.30pm
Brahms *Piano Concerto No. 2*
Beethoven (arr. Mahler) *Symphony No. 3*

Vladimir Jurowski *conductor*
Leif Ove Andsnes *piano*

Wednesday 1 December 2010 | 7.30pm
Debussy (orch. Colin Matthews)
Préludes (selection)
Britten *Les Illuminations*
Mahler *Symphony No. 4*

Vladimir Jurowski *conductor*
Christine Schäfer *soprano*

Saturday 4 December 2010 | 7.30pm
Beethoven *Piano Concerto No. 4*
Mahler *Symphony No. 1 (original version
including Blumine)*

Vladimir Jurowski *conductor*
Hélène Grimaud *piano*

Vladimir Jurowski ©Roman Gontcharov

www.lpo.org.uk

**RESIDENT AT
SOUTHBANK
CENTRE**

Bach

BITES

It's difficult not to be moved by the powerful musical genius of J. S. Bach. Lindsay Kemp introduces this season's Bach Day, which offers three snapshots of the composer's diverse output, from the Brandenburg Concertos to full-scale orchestral transcriptions

It would take a long day indeed to present all that is great about Johann Sebastian Bach. This, after all, is an art which encompasses the joyousness of the Brandenburg Concertos, the nobility of the Cello Suites and the glowing splendour of the Mass in B minor, as well as the deep human sympathies of the *St Matthew Passion*, the mixture of certainty and humble beauty that pervades the church cantatas and the dizzying intellectual accomplishments of contrapuntal masterpieces such as the 'Goldberg' Variations or *The Art of Fugue*. It is hardly to be demonstrated in just a few hours, then.

So what can we glean from this year's Proms Bach Day (Saturday 14 August), other than the deep pleasure and satisfaction of spending time with the most powerful musical mind there has ever been? Maybe the answer lies in the three varied snapshots that these concerts offer – richly coloured images that reveal not only aspects of the composer's music, but also intriguing glimpses of the man himself.

Bach's life was not without frustrations. In the years from 1723 until his death – when he was in charge of the music at St Thomas's Church, Leipzig – he frequently came into conflict with his employers, and the musicians he had to work with were not always of the highest calibre.

This did not stop him from writing great music, of course, but he had a happier time in his previous post, as Kapellmeister to the Cöthen court from 1717. Prince Leopold of Anhalt-Cöthen, Bach's employer there, was a keen musician and a good friend, and it was for his small orchestra of fine instrumentalists that Bach created the six works now known as the Brandenburg Concertos, the subject of two matinee concerts offered by Sir John Eliot Gardiner and the English Baroque Soloists. To picture these exuberant pieces being performed by Bach and his colleagues – maybe with the composer himself cutting loose in the Fifth Concerto's brilliant solo harpsichord cadenza – is to see a figure far removed from the persona drawn in his famously stiff portraits.

Bach's brilliance as a keyboard performer served him throughout his career. It is how he made his name as a young man in the towns and cities of northern Germany, and in the organ music he wrote at this time the flamboyance of youth is seldom far from the surface. But if Bach was no stranger to the idea of showing off as a performer, he also knew how to dazzle with compositional technique, as he showed in the famous Passacaglia and Fugue in C minor – 20 variations on a short bass-line figure (21 if you count the superb concluding fugue) – which opens David Briggs's late-afternoon recital on the Royal Albert Hall organ. Bach was also happy to bring non-organ music to the instrument, as for instance when, at the end of his life, he transcribed various vocal numbers from his church cantatas, including the chorus familiar in English-speaking countries as 'Sleepers, awake!'. It means we need have no qualms about enjoying more recent organ transcriptions of vocal pieces by Stainton de B. Taylor and Virgil Fox, or even Briggs's own arrangement of the Third Orchestral Suite, with the so-called 'Air on the G String' at its heart.

Pragmatism of this kind is actually another important part of Bach's personality. The times when he transferred his own music from one medium to another are many, and perhaps he would have agreed with Busoni's claim that 'every notation is, in itself, the transcription of an abstract idea'. But if the question remains about exactly what that

St Thomas's Church in Leipzig, where Bach was Kapellmeister from 1723 until his death

essential idea is, it is not difficult to see what inspired the numerous musicians who have made orchestral arrangements of Bach's music over the years, some of whom feature in an evening concert given by Andrew Litton and the Royal Philharmonic Orchestra. Leopold Stokowski, himself once a shamelessly fiery organist, made the most famous transcription of all in his vivid realisation of the somewhat gothic Toccata and Fugue in D minor; Italian colourist Ottorino Respighi clearly enjoyed enlarging the already powerful accumulation of sonority that is the C minor Passacaglia and Fugue; and Granville Bantock clearly warmed to the mellow melodic undulations of 'Sleepers, awake!'. The same concert also sees Bach-based commissions from newcomers Alissa Firsova and Tarik O'Regan, who have taken as inspiration a movement from the sonatas for viola da gamba and solo violin respectively. Like their predecessors they can rest assured that they are working with the very best of materials. ●

Lindsay Kemp is a producer for BBC Radio 3, Artistic Director of the Lufthansa Festival of Baroque Music and a regular contributor to *Gramophone*.

okg-images: Berlin State Library, Germany/Bridgeman Art Library; Shutterstock; Lebrecht Music & Arts (p68); Lebrecht Music & Arts (p68 signature); okg-images (above right); ColouriseAL/Lebrecht Music & Arts (below right)

BACH DAY AT THE PROMS
Saturday 14 August

Proms Saturday Matinee 1,
11.30am, Cadogan Hall
Brandenburg Concertos Nos. 1, 4 & 6
English Baroque Soloists
Sir John Eliot Gardiner *conductor*

Proms Saturday Matinee 2,
1.30pm, Cadogan Hall
Brandenburg Concertos Nos. 2, 3 & 5
English Baroque Soloists
Sir John Eliot Gardiner *conductor*

Prom 38, 5.00pm, Royal Albert Hall
Organ recital David Briggs *organ*

Prom 39, 7.30pm, Royal Albert Hall
Orchestral transcriptions/ arrangements of Bach by Bantock, Alissa Firsova, Grainger, Tarik O'Regan, Respighi, Sargent, Stokowski, Walton and Wood
Royal Philharmonic Orchestra
Andrew Litton *conductor*

10TH ANNIVERSARY SEASON BOX OFFICE 020 7935 2141 ONLINE BOOKING WWW.WIGMORE-HALL.ORG.UK

2010-2011
SEPTEMBER 10 – JULY 11
WIGMORE SERIES

DANIEL BARENBOIM | JOSHUA BELL | STEVEN ISSERLIS | DAME MITSUKO UCHIDA
MARTHA ARGERICH | STEPHEN KOVACEVICH | ELISABETH LEONSKAJA | JONAS KAUFMANN
JOHN WILLIAMS | EMERSON STRING QUARTET | ALINA IBRAGIMOVA | NASH ENSEMBLE
MARK PADMORE | BRAD MEHLDAU | JERUSALEM QUARTET | KATE ROYAL | IAN BOSTRIDGE
ACADEMY OF ANCIENT MUSIC | KARITA MATTILA | THOMAS HAMPSON | LEIF OVE ANDSNES
QUATUOR MOSAÏQUES | MARIA JOÃO PIRES | ALICE COOTE | TAKÁCS QUARTET | ANDRÁS SCHIFF
BELCEA QUARTET | MATTHIAS GOERNE | THOMAS QUASTHOFF | MARTIN FRÖST | ANGELA HEWITT

**Wigmore Series September – December is now on sale. For full details and to book tickets
call the Box Office on 020 7935 2141 or visit www.wigmore-hall.org.uk**
For a free brochure email brochure@wigmore-hall.org.uk with your postal address (quoting 'BBC Proms') or call the Box Office

Following last year's hit tribute to MGM musicals, this season the Proms marks 50 years since the death of Oscar Hammerstein II – regarded by many as 'America's poet laureate' – and the 80th birthday of the uncannily talented tunesmith and wordsmith, Stephen Sondheim. Edward Seckerson salutes their contributions to Broadway and the world stage

Bring on
BROADWAY

Stephen Sondheim has often said of his mentor and surrogate father Oscar Hammerstein II that where he really excelled was in the romantic stuff. Hammerstein didn't just write in his lyrics about 'the bright golden haze on the meadow': he could see it, smell it, feel it. It *really was* a beautiful morning, and he was going to tell us why. To Sondheim, of course, the imagery was a little too ripe, too fanciful. Heaven forbid the hills should ever be alive with the sound of music; and, far from pacifying children of all ages, Sondheim's own 'favourite things' would very likely scare them to death. Yet these two very different men were inextricably bonded by a mutual desire to push back the boundaries of where musical theatre could take us, to tell stories and to create songs that became an integral part of those stories, not just a series of entertaining diversions along the way.

Even Hammerstein's beginnings in the rarefied and fragrant world of operetta reflected a desire to sharpen the storytelling – though one has to wonder how a young lyricist fashioning his 'Indian Love Call' from *Rose-Marie* (1924) around the line 'When I'm calling you-oo-oo-oo …' ever really expected to have his call returned. It was hardly auspicious. But then again the 'oo' syllables cooed so easily and so memorably with composer Rudolf Friml's romantic waftings that a major hit was pretty much inevitable. Doors really started opening for Hammerstein after that, and all of them eventually led to a show that unforgettably fused operetta traditions with a brave new Broadway vernacular: *Show Boat* (1927) was quite simply without precedent in the history of American musical comedy; the complexity and seriousness of Hammerstein's book and the sheer richness and scale of Jerome Kern's score set the bar dauntingly high.

But then along came Richard Rodgers, and the wholesale transformation of American musical theatre began in earnest with the Pulitzer Prize-winning *Oklahoma!* (1943). Everything Hammerstein

Richard Rodgers (*left*) and Oscar Hammerstein II: the composer–lyricist duo who defined the Broadway musicals of the 1940s and 1950s

Hammerstein and Sondheim were inextricably bonded by a mutual desire to push back the boundaries of where musical theatre could take us.

had learnt about advancing all the elements of a musical into a single unified whole came to fruition here. Broadway's new dawn was serenaded from offstage by the show's hero Curly as he lazily rode his way through that corn 'as high as an elephant's eye'. But there were bigger themes at work in this remarkable show, not least among them the birth of the nation's 46th state. Small wonder Hammerstein became dubbed 'America's Poet Laureate'. He idealised his country but he was not afraid to act as its social conscience, too. Rodgers and Hammerstein's collaboration embraced 'difficult' subjects: domestic violence in *Carousel* (1945), medical ethics and big business in the experimental *Allegro* (1947), racism and war in *South Pacific* (1949), cultural differences in *The King and I* (1951). But they did so with such sleight of hand and whole-hearted strength of purpose that their adoring audiences were blissfully unaware of how skilfully their emotions were being manipulated. Rodgers's aching melodies played a big part in that, of course, and in choosing to showcase the opulent movie orchestrations for this year's Rodgers and Hammerstein Prom (22 August), John Wilson and his fabulous orchestra – who together

created a sensation last summer with their MGM musicals extravaganza – will once again be spiriting us back to the studio sound stages, where the arranging genius of Alfred Newman first achieved cinemascopic splendour.

In musicals, the biggest decision that composers and lyricists repeatedly have to make is where to sing and why. The old maxim that people sing when the emotional stakes are so high they can no longer speak is not one to which Hammerstein, and certainly not Sondheim, have ever wholly subscribed. If Sondheim has always sought to subvert expectations, Hammerstein has tended to invert them. This he proved in the 'conditional' love duets: 'If I Loved You' from *Carousel*; and 'People Will Say We're in Love' from *Oklahoma!*, where the series of 'don'ts' in the lyric are ingeniously mirrored in the middle eight or 'release' of the song, in which Rodgers simply inverts the melody.

Then there are instances where the entire drama effectively turns on a single number: take the 'Soliloquy' from *Carousel*, which represents the most exciting fusion of words, music and dramaturgy in any Rodgers and Hammerstein show. This is the sequence where the ne'er-do-well Billy Bigalow reflects on fatherhood and in so doing seeks to justify the life-changing decisions he now has to make. Musically, there is enough material in this 10-minute span for an entire score – Rodgers at his glorious best – while Hammerstein's lyrics characterise Billy's hyperactive shifts of thought, mood and deed to brilliant effect. Sondheim has cited this scene as pivotal in demonstrating what musical theatre can achieve. He openly admits that it was the inspiration for his own Sweeney Todd's 'Epiphany' – equally not so much a song as a *scena*, in which Sweeney resolves to practise his way to Judge Turpin's throat. ▶

Poster for the 1963 London production of *A Funny Thing Happened on the Way to the Forum*, featuring Frankie Howerd, which ran for 762 performances

Context is all in Sondheim's shows and, because he'd be the first to admit that his songs work best serving the dramatic purpose for which they were designed, David Charles Abell – who conducts the Sondheim 80th-birthday Prom (31 July) – has devised a series of telling juxtapositions to act as snapshots of the bigger drama. 'Epiphany' from *Sweeney Todd* is one and, if anyone ever thought they could second-guess Sondheim, then what follows this momentous sequence will surely have proved them wrong. Any other composer/lyricist would have seen 'Epiphany' as the big Act 1 curtain but Sondheim wickedly pulls the rug from beneath our expectations, undercutting the high melodrama with a savagely funny music-hall turn entitled 'A Little Priest', where Sweeney and Mrs Lovett chew over the potential for human pie-fillings and we're sent out into the interval a little light-headed, a little queasy and in no doubt as to where Act 2 will be taking us.

Sondheim's dramatic instincts are extraordinary; his love of theatre, his passion for the craftsmanship of fine writing and the possibilities of what that can achieve is evident in all his pieces; the dazzling erudition of his lyrics bears endless repetition. But not enough is said and written about Sondheim the composer, and the balance needs redressing. The musical voice may be easy to parody – the best always are – but at least that voice is his own.

But how to describe it? A free and refreshing lyricism underpinned by a restless desire to move on? The trademark repeated rhythms to some extent reflect Sondheim's own impatience for what comes next; and, of course, they accentuate the imperative of the songs – like the timepiece effect that underpins the verse of 'Our Time' from *Merrily We Roll Along* or the industrial drive of progress that characterises 'Next' from *Pacific Overtures*.

But there is time to reflect, too, and in *Passion*, Sondheim's most effusively romantic score, the profound yearning of songs like 'Loving You' takes us to the same place, though by different means, that Rodgers and Hammerstein inhabited in *Carousel*. There's the same ache, albeit subtly subverted, in the ecstatic love duet 'Too Many Mornings' from *Follies* because this duet is only an impossible dream of what might have been. And, speaking of what might have been, Sondheim's capacity to surprise and wrong-foot us can throw up deliciously anti-romantic notions – as in the duet 'Agony' from *Into the Woods*, which tells us that it ain't all wine and roses being a Prince in a fairy tale.

None of these songs could have been written by anybody else, none of these tunes (*pace* the 'Sondheim doesn't write tunes' brigade) could have come from another pen – but, more importantly, they are the right songs and the right tunes for the drama they serve. And you can't help but feel something stirring deep inside you as the living realisation of Georges Seurat's painting *A Sunday Afternoon on the Island of La Grande Jatte* finally comes together in 'Sunday' – the stonking Act 1 finale of *Sunday in the Park with George*. ●

Writer and journalist Edward Seckerson is a critic for *The Independent* and for many years wrote and presented BBC Radio 3's *Stage and Screen* programme. He is a regular contributor to numerous magazines and podcasts.

Johnny Depp as the 'Demon Barber of Fleet Street' in Tim Burton's recent film remake (2007) of Sondheim's *Sweeney Todd*

Stephen Sondheim: today's king of Broadway musicals

MUSICAL THEATRE AT THE PROMS

Sondheim at 80
Prom 19, 31 July
Including excerpts from *Follies*, *A Funny Thing Happened on the Way to the Forum*, *A Little Night Music*, *Sunday in the Park with George* and *Sweeney Todd*
Soloists, BBC Concert Orchestra
David Charles Abell *conductor*

A Celebration of Rodgers & Hammerstein
Prom 49, 22 August
Including excerpts from *Carousel*, *The King and I*, *Oklahoma!*, *The Sound of Music* and *South Pacific*
Soloists, John Wilson Orchestra
John Wilson *conductor*

The return of the Doctor Who Prom, following the Time Lord's Proms debut in 2008, is only one of a number of Proms which all the family can enjoy, as **Clara Nissen** explains

There are few things more awe-inspiring than a full, 100-strong orchestra in the hands of a charismatic conductor, giving some stick to a movement from a Shostakovich symphony. But add into the equation a range of dance styles, including cool Afro-Brazilian capoeira, or aliens charging down the aisles of the Royal Albert Hall, and you've got something even better: a family-friendly Prom.

You might imagine that bringing your children to the average classical concert would leave them bored and fidgety, prompting the dreaded question, 'Are we going home yet?' Every Prom is designed to be a unique event, to which children aged 5 upwards are welcome. But bringing your kids to a more informal concert, designed specially for young people, might just help them make a giant leap towards a life-long enjoyment of music – as well as offering a great day out.

Since the very first dedicated children's Prom in 1998, we've learnt that kids love the spectacle, the big orchestras, the noises and the humongous Royal Albert Hall; and, from the feedback received, we know that these concerts are really memorable occasions for many in the audience. The recipe for success lies in short, contrasting and exciting pieces

DEEP **IMPACT**

that show the breadth of classical music, all introduced by a friendly presenter. Then throw in the odd surprise …

'The Daleks have travelled back in time and kidnapped Henry Wood. From now on, the Proms will only play DALEK MUSIC!' This was the threat uttered by the Dalek who, along with other aliens both hostile and friendly, took over the Royal Albert Hall at a special Doctor Who Prom in 2008. Having played host to dinosaurs (yes, moving ones!) last year in the Evolution! Prom, the Hall this year is once again the target of alien domination when Doctor Who returns for Proms 10 and 11.

Hosted by Karen Gillan (the Doctor's companion) and Matt Smith (the Doctor), these concerts feature the combined might of the BBC National Orchestra of Wales and the London Philharmonic Choir under

'The Daleks have travelled back in time and kidnapped Henry Wood. From now on, the Proms will only play DALEK MUSIC!'

conductors Ben Foster and Grant Llewellyn. As well as music from the *Doctor Who* series (composed by Murray Gold), Gillan and Smith will introduce classical favourites relating to the theme of time, space and travel, including Wagner's *Ride of the Valkyries*, John Adams's *Short Ride in a Fast Machine* and 'Mars' from Holst's *The Planets*.

And for Prom 59 the dynamic Aurora Orchestra under Principal Conductor Nicholas Collon will swell in size, as it is joined by the National Children's Chamber and National Youth Chamber orchestras. Fast gaining a reputation for its energetic and innovative programmes, the Aurora Orchestra and friends will be presenting a vast range of repertoire – from Rimsky-Korsakov's fiendishly fast *Flight of the Bumblebee* to Satie's relaxed and spacious *Gymnopédie* No. 1, and from French 17th-century Lully to Soviet Shostakovich – all bound

together with a dance theme. With a sprinkling of opportunities for participation – you might find yourself being part of a huge animal soundscape, for instance – you'll also get an introduction to the instruments of the orchestra. It should be an aural and visual spectacular, and watch out for some unusual goings-on within the auditorium, too!

Looking through the listings for this summer's Proms (*see pages 110–148*), you may well feel tempted to explore some of the other concerts in the season – and why not, when you remember that all seats for 5- to 16-year-olds are half price (except for the Last Night) – and Promming tickets (standing in the Arena or Gallery) are still a snip at £5.00. There are some inspiring offerings to mull over, such as the musicals of Stephen Sondheim (Prom 19) and of Rodgers and Hammerstein (Prom 49), as well as British and American classics from the BBC Concert Orchestra under the baton of the Boston Pops Orchestra's Keith Lockhart (Prom 60). If you want to make more of a day of it, you could choose a family-friendly Proms Plus event (*see pages 88–91*) – a great way to get to know some of the music to be heard later in the evening – and then attend the Prom afterwards.

The BBC Proms is the ideal place to introduce your family to the imaginative world of classical music. So drag your kids away from the small-screen world of social networking websites and video games, and transport them to new musical horizons. ●

Clara Nissen is Sub-Editor, BBC Proms Publications.

FAMILY CONCERTS AT THE PROMS

Doctor Who Prom
Proms 10 & 11 (24 July, 7.30pm & 25 July, 11.00am)
Music from the BBC TV series, plus classical favourites on the theme of time, space and travel

Children's Prom
Prom 59 (30 August, 11.00am)
A wide-ranging programme designed to show off the scale and variety of the classical symphony orchestra

See also Prom 19 (31 July, 7.30pm), Prom 49 (22 August, 4.00pm), Prom 60 (30 August, 7.00pm)

TOP: Up close and personal with a dinosaur at last year's Evolution! Prom; **ABOVE:** the evil Davros pays a visit at the Doctor Who Prom in 2008

Chris Christodoulou/BBC

Autumn 2010
AT ENO

EN
O

FAUST
Gounod

A dramatic new staging by
Des McAnuff, conducted
by Edward Gardner
○ 18 Sep – 16 Oct

THE MAKROPULOS
CASE
Janáček

Christopher Alden's
Olivier Award-nominated
production returns
○ 20 Sep – 5 Oct

RADAMISTO
Handel

David Alden returns
following his South Bank
Show Award-winning
production of *Peter Grimes*
○ 7 Oct – 4 Nov

LA BOHÈME
Puccini

Jonathan Miller's acclaimed
production of Puccini's
tragic masterpiece returns
○ 18 Oct – 25 Nov

DON GIOVANNI
Mozart

Rufus Norris directs this
much-loved masterpiece
with set designs by regular
collaborator Ian MacNeil
○ 6 Nov – 3 Dec

A DOG'S HEART
Raskatov

Complicité's Simon
McBurney directs this
sharp, absurdist satire
○ 20 Nov – 4 Dec

ENO Friends booking
opens Monday 19 April

ENO Subscription booking
opens Monday 26 April

General booking opens
Monday 10 May

www.eno.org
0871 911 0200

Supported by
**ARTS COUNCIL
ENGLAND**

La bohème directed by Jonathan Miller
Photograph: Tristram Kenton

NEW DISCOVERIES

This year there are more ways than ever to get involved in activities for all the family. Proms Learning Manager Ellara Wakely surveys the options

The Proms offers an exciting journey for anyone who wants to take part this season, from those making their first steps into the festival to regulars returning to participate for another year. Begin your Proms Learning experience with your family and friends – or come along and make new ones – at one of the workshops in our newly extended Music Intro series; or enjoy special events such as children's concerts and Proms Out+About. You can also join in our Proms Family Orchestra and Chorus and Come and Sing Wagner events, broaden your musical horizons in the BBC Proms Inspire scheme for young composers, or sign up for an RCM Sparks course – part of a new partnership with the Royal College of Music. The Proms continues to develop quality, creative learning opportunities, and what better way to build on these projects than by commissioning two

exciting new works, one from a former winner of the Inspire Young Composers' Competition and the other by British composer Graham Fitkin, specially written for the Proms Family Orchestra to perform alongside the BBC Concert Orchestra. Read on to find out more about what's on offer and how to get involved …

BBC Proms Inspire – nurturing young composers
There aren't many 15-year-olds who can say they've had their music played to an audience of 40 million, but last year's Proms Inspire scheme meant just that for the six lucky winners of the Inspire Young Composers' Competition, who were commissioned to write fanfares for the Last Night of the Proms. Broadcast across the world and performed live around the UK – from the cavernous Royal Albert Hall to the five open-air Proms in the Park events across the country – it was an experience none of them is likely to forget.

This year's Inspire scheme was launched in February with hundreds of young composers participating in nationwide Composer Labs taking place from Cornwall to Glasgow, with plenty of stops in between. The Composer Labs embody the ethos of the scheme, which aims to inspire young people aged 12 to 18 to harness their creativity and help them to write their own music, at the same time offering unique chances for them to hear their music performed. Participants of the scheme work with professional musicians and composers, meet other budding composers and even record new works. And, for those who didn't get the chance to attend a Lab earlier this year, for the first time there is an online Composer Lab that can be accessed by all at bbc.co.uk/proms.

Everyone who has taken part in the scheme this year will be invited to take part in BBC Proms Inspire Day on Monday 2 August. After a series of workshop sessions, the winning pieces of the 2010 Inspire Young Composers' Competition will be ▶

Inspire

Do you know someone who should be entering the BBC Proms Inspire Young Composers' Competition for 12- to 18-year-olds?

The deadline for entries is Friday 28 May 2010

The BBC Proms Inspire Day 2010, including the Inspire Young Composers' Concert at the Royal College of Music (5.30pm–6.30pm), will be held on Monday 2 August. *Please note: capacity for the concert is very limited.*

For more details, visit bbc.co.uk/proms, email promslearning@bbc.co.uk or call 020 7765 0643

DATES FOR YOUR DIARY

Proms Out+About
Westfield London, Ariel Way, London W12 7GF
Friday 9 July, 6.30pm–8.00pm

Family Music Intro*†
Royal College of Music, Prince Consort Road, London SW7 2BS
Friday 23 July, 5.30pm–6.30pm
Thursday 29 July, 5.00pm–6.00pm
Tuesday 10 August, 5.30pm–6.30pm
Wednesday 18 August, 5.30pm–6.30pm
Sunday 22 August, 5.30pm–6.30pm
Thursday 26 August, 5.00pm–6.00pm
Monday 30 August, 5.00pm–6.00pm

Music Intro†
Royal College of Music
Friday 30 July, 5.45pm–6.30pm
Wednesday 4 August, 5.15pm–6.00pm
Friday 6 August, 5.15pm–6.00pm
Thursday 12 August, 5.45pm–6.30pm
Friday 13 August, 5.45pm–6.30pm
Friday 20 August, 5.15pm–6.00pm
Tuesday 7 September, 5.45pm–6.30pm

Proms Family Orchestra and Chorus*‡
Royal College of Music
Saturday 24 July, 2.00pm–4.00pm
Sunday 25 July, 1.45pm–3.30pm
Saturday 31 July, 1.00pm–3.00pm
Sunday 15 August, 1.00pm–3.00pm
Sunday 22 August, 1.00pm–3.00pm
Monday 30 August, 1.30pm–3.30pm

Proms Family Orchestra Play at the Proms
If you and your family are enthusiastic musicians who live in Cornwall or London, visit bbc.co.uk/proms to find out how you could find yourselves playing alongside the BBC Concert Orchestra at the Proms this summer.

Come and Sing Wagner‡ & Wagner Study Session‡
Royal College of Music
Saturday 17 July, 11.00am–1.00pm

All events are free
* For family members aged 7 upwards
† Turn up early to secure your place
‡ Places must be booked in advance: visit bbc.co.uk/proms or call 020 7765 0643

Unsuspecting shoppers at Westfield London hear the BBC Symphony Orchestra perform as part of last year's Out+About

performed by the Aurora Orchestra at a special Proms Plus concert at the Royal College of Music (broadcast later that week on BBC Radio 3). On Saturday 14 August (Prom 39) you can hear a new Proms commission by former Inspire Young Composers' Competition winner Alissa Firsova: her Bach-inspired new work adds an up-to-the-minute twist to Bach Day. (*See panel, page 83, for how to apply.*)

'I made it to Westfield and was lucky enough to see last night's concert. I feel extremely lucky that I made it from work in time and thoroughly enjoyed the whole event.'

Audience member, Out+About 2009

Proms Out+About

Proms Out+About continues to seek out new audiences in an eclectic range of venues. The recipe is simple: take a full-sized orchestra, leading artists and a conductor and offer new audiences a free performance as a taste of the season to come. On Friday 9 July the BBC Symphony Orchestra will be returning to Westfield London for a Prom with a difference. Expect the unexpected, including the opportunity to take part yourself. To find out more, visit bbc.co.uk/proms.

Family Music Intro, Music Intro and RCM Sparks

The ethos of the Proms has always been to appeal to the widest possible audience. Everyone aged 5 and upwards is welcome for all concerts and under-16s are offered half-price tickets (except the Last Night).

For half a decade Family Music Intro – part of the Proms Plus series (*see pages 88–91*) – has been helping introduce families to the Proms and classical music. A selection of specially chosen concerts is preceded by dynamic, participatory workshops, revealing the stories and highlights of the forthcoming Prom and introducing some of the musicians. Drawing on the success of the Family Music Intro series, a new Music Intro series will run this year, aimed at adults who are new to classical music, featuring live musical extracts played by some of the evening's musicians. We're certain that anyone attending a Music Intro event this season will know a lot more about the pieces by the time they take their seats at the following concert.

The Proms has also joined up this year with RCM Sparks, the Royal College of Music's learning scheme, which will be offering an exciting array of workshops for 6- to 18-year-olds linked to this year's Proms season. (*For details, see panel opposite.*)

Proms Family Orchestra and Chorus

Following the debut of the Proms Family Orchestra and Chorus at the Proms last year, this season sees a new Cornwall-themed commission from Graham Fitkin for the Cornwall- and London-based Proms Family Orchestra and Chorus to perform alongside the BBC Concert Orchestra on Monday 30 August (Prom 60). The Proms Family Orchestra and Chorus invite families, whatever their shape and size, to join the musicians of the Proms in playing music together. The Family Orchestra and Chorus embody the spirit of the Proms – it doesn't matter if you're a first-timer or a virtuoso, the result is thrilling music-making that can make it all the way to the Proms stage and BBC Radio 3.

Proms Family Orchestra and Chorus workshops take place throughout the season with a number of one-off sessions programmed alongside Proms that we think that you and your family might enjoy. Led by Lincoln Abbotts and our team of professional musicians, the Proms Family Orchestra and Chorus are open to all family members, from those who have never played or sung before to budding musicians and rusty returners. Proms Family Orchestra and Chorus events are a great way to enjoy playing music together as a family, while also exploring music in a fresh and exciting way. (*For details, see panel, page 83.*)

Come and Sing Wagner and the Wagner Study Session

With opera featuring strongly in this year's Proms festival, we'll be celebrating opera on Saturday 17 July. Anyone aged 16 and over is invited to join members of Welsh National Opera in a Come and Sing Wagner event. There's also the opportunity to explore *The Mastersingers of Nuremberg* in more depth with John Deathridge and Tim Blanning in a Wagner Study Session. (*For details, see panel, page 83.*) ●

'The whole experience was fantastic for young and old, and the excitement among all was testament to this. We can't wait for the next project.'

Participant, Proms Family Orchestra 2009

The audience at last year's Indian Voices in the Park enjoys music from the Proms Family Orchestra

Simon Jay Price/BBC (p84 & below left); Chris Christodoulou/BBC (above right)

A 2009 Proms Family Orchestra member poses with the bust of Henry Wood

'We all had a fantastic time. It was a great opportunity to play as a family, with other families, and a wonderful learning experience for everyone.'

Participant, Proms Family Orchestra 2009

RCM SPARKS SUMMER MUSIC 2010

The Learning and Participation Department at the Royal College of Music has teamed up with the BBC Proms to develop a programme of music activities for 6- to 18-year-olds. When visiting the Proms this summer, why not hop across the road to the Royal College of Music? Whether it's playing, composing or uncovering treasures in the museum or library, RCM Sparks is providing opportunities for everyone to engage in Proms-related musical activities.

Summer Music Workshops – for ages 6 to 12

27 July; 3, 10, 18 & 26 August, 11.30am–4.30pm

Play and sing, compose and create, bang and shake! These fun, hands-on workshops offer both beginners and more experienced players the opportunity to take part in live music-making while learning more about music featured in this year's Proms. Why not enjoy a whole day of incredible music-making by combining three activities in one: Sparks Summer Music workshop (daytime), Proms Family Music Intro (early evening) and Prom (evening)?

Summer Springboard – short courses for ages 13 to 18

Ages 13–15: 28–30 July (including a visit to Prom 16 on 29 July)
Ages 16–18: 4–6 August (including a visit to Prom 24 on 4 August)
Kick-start your summer with some inspirational music-making. With the support of workshop leaders and a team of young RCM musicians, improvise, jam, compose, create and perform a new piece inspired by music from the Proms. For all abilities and musical styles.

Fantastic Journeys Workshop – for ages 10 to 15

7 August, 2.00pm–6.30pm (including taking part in a performance at Proms Plus event)
The RCM and Proms team up with the National Youth Orchestra of Great Britain for a special workshop exploring the fantasy themes in Prom 29. Whatever your level, bring your instrument along and create your own music alongside members of the NYO.

Discovery Sessions

Throughout the summer, 3.30pm–4.30pm*
Join us in the RCM's famed museum and library to explore some of the college's hidden treasures, from manuscript scores and original letters to ancient instruments and music-related portraits. Discovery Sessions link closely to Proms, adding an extra dimension to your concert experience.

*Visit www.rcm.ac.uk/summermusic for full listings

RCM Sparks is the Royal College of Music's Learning and Participation programme. For more information about RCM Sparks, visit www.rcm.ac.uk/sparks or call 020 7591 4394.

All RCM Sparks events are free but must be booked in advance. For more information visit www.rcm.ac.uk/summermusic. To book, call 020 7591 4314.

SHELL CLASSIC INTERNATIONAL 2010/11

GREAT ORCHESTRAS FROM AROUND THE WORLD
ROYAL FESTIVAL HALL

Spira Mirabilis © Karen Robinson

Sir Simon Rattle © Monika Rittershaus

TERESA CARREÑO YOUTH ORCHESTRA OF VENEZUELA

CHRISTIAN VÁSQUEZ conductor

Tuesday 12 October 2010
Thursday 14 October 2010

SPIRA MIRABILIS

Beethoven Symphony No.3 (Eroica)

Friday 5 November 2010
Queen Elizabeth Hall

BUDAPEST FESTIVAL ORCHESTRA

IVÁN FISCHER conductor
STEPHEN HOUGH piano

Haydn Symphony No.92 (Oxford)
Liszt Piano Concerto No.1 in E flat
Beethoven Symphony No.6 (Pastoral)

Sunday 16 January 2011

BERLINER PHILHARMONIKER

SIR SIMON RATTLE conductor

Sunday 20 February 2011
Wednesday 23 February 2011

RETURNS ONLY

Media partner

THE TIMES

Supported by
ARTS COUNCIL ENGLAND

BAVARIAN RADIO SYMPHONY ORCHESTRA

MARISS JANSONS conductor
MITSUKO UCHIDA piano

Beethoven Piano Concerto No.3
Strauss Ein Heldenleben

Friday 25 March 2011

SOLOISTS OF BAVARIAN RADIO SYMPHONY ORCHESTRA

MITSUKO UCHIDA piano

Beethoven Quintet in E flat for piano and wind, Op.16
Schubert Octet, D.803

Sunday 27 March 2011
Queen Elizabeth Hall

BERLIN STAATSKAPELLE

PIERRE BOULEZ conductor
DANIEL BARENBOIM piano

Wagner Eine Faust-Ouvertüre
Liszt Piano Concerto No.2 in A
Wagner Siegfried Idyll
Liszt Piano Concerto No.1 in E flat

Monday 13 June 2011

TICKETS 0844 847 9934
WWW.SOUTHBANKCENTRE.CO.UK

SOUTHBANK CENTRE

Proms
PLUS

Christopher Cook outlines this year's Proms Plus series – the festival-within-a-festival whose talks, workshops and other pre-concert events offer a lively introduction to the music and artists featured during the season

Why do we go to the BBC Proms? To face the music, of course, in the unique summer atmosphere of the Royal Albert Hall, whether sitting, standing or (if you want to) lying down in the Gallery.

Another question: why have so many of us been hurrying to South Kensington two hours before a concert? The answer: we've caught the Proms Plus bug. We want to know more about the music and the musicians who are part of the world's most magnificent music festival and to think in broader ways about what we are going to hear in the nation's village hall.

With its beginnings in the mid-1970s as introductions to only a handful of Proms in the Royal Albert Hall, the programme of pre-Prom events mushroomed in 2008 into a festival-within-a-festival, now with a home of its own – the Amaryllis Fleming Concert Hall in the Royal College of Music. Walk down the steps to the south of the Royal Albert Hall, cross Prince Consort Road, and before you stands the Royal College of Music – a red-brick building dressed with buff-coloured Weldon stone.

Here, every day during the season – and sometimes several times in the course of a weekend – you can join the Proms Plus audience, usually before the main evening concert. And it's absolutely free: all part of the BBC's mission to inform and to educate as well as entertain.

You don't even need a ticket for the concert to get into Proms Plus, but every event is arranged to finish in time for the audience to saunter back up to the Royal Albert Hall for the following Prom. A word of advice though: get to the Royal College as early as you can (doors open 30 minutes before the event starts). Admission to most Proms Plus events is on a 'first come, first served' basis and popular events can fill up quickly.

So you'll have to arrive in good time on 31 July if you want to hear the man who reinvented the American musical. Stephen Sondheim is 80 this year and there's a Prom to wish a happy birthday to a composer who has criss-crossed his way between popular and art music so magnificently for nearly 60 years since he wrote the lyrics for *West Side Story*.

Gathered together under the single title of Proms Plus is a family of six kinds of events: Proms Intro, Composer Portraits, Proms Literary Festival, Music Intro (new this year), Family Music Intro and Proms Family Orchestra and Chorus (*see Proms Plus Events box, right*). The Proms season brings a host of special musical events and marks musical anniversaries, and where the platform leads, Proms Plus follows. So former newsreader and presenter John Suchet – also a Beethoven biographer – raises the curtain on Paul Lewis's cycle of Beethoven piano concertos (21 July); and Sir John Eliot Gardiner discusses Monteverdi's *Vespers of 1610* before he conducts the work (10 September).

The chief pleasure of the Proms Literary Festival is that it never tries to track the music that we're going to hear in the Hall but walks a parallel line. So when the BBC Symphony Orchestra plays Prokofiev and Shostakovich on 22 July, the Literary Festival remembers that it's the 150th anniversary of Anton Chekhov's birth and starts a mini Russian season of its own. Then on 1 August the novelist

Shakespeare's star-crossed lovers, Romeo and Juliet, feature in a Proms Literary Festival event on 1 August tracing the history of love

Howard Jacobson joins classical scholar Mary Beard to explore the idea of romantic love before a Prom that includes the love scene from Berlioz's *Romeo and Juliet* and Act 2 of Wagner's *Tristan and Isolde*. And before Humperdinck's Hänsel and Gretel disappear into the woods on 31 August, Anne Fine, a former Children's Laureate, and the psychotherapist Margaret Rustin dig deep into this favourite folk tale collected by the Brothers Grimm. What can it say to young and old, to children and their parents today? What makes the Proms Literary Festival doubly refreshing is that none of its guests is there to 'push' their latest publication.

Proms Plus has always pushed the boat out for new music, particularly so in the Composer Portraits. This year Tansy Davies, James Dillon, Colin Matthews and Huw Watkins – all of whom have premieres this season – will be talking about their music alongside live performances of their work. The Composer Portrait on 17 August promises us something a little bit special: Huw Watkins is a distinguished pianist as well as a composer, and he'll be playing his own music that night with musicians from the Royal College of Music. ▶

Andy Potts (p88 illustration): Whitworth Art Gallery/University of Manchester/Bridgeman Art Library (above right); State Tretyakov Gallery, Moscow/Bridgeman Art Library (below right)

PROMS PLUS EVENTS

Proms Intro events feature conductors, musicians, composers and experts in conversation about the music featured in the following Prom.

Composer Portraits feature chamber music by leading composers, each of whom will have a work premiered in the same day's Prom.

Proms Literary Festival explores themes of the Proms season and the relationship between writers and composers.

Music Intro workshops are jargon-free introductions to the music of the evening's Prom, with live music from some of the evening's performers. Great for first-timers.

Family Music Intro workshops are aimed at children aged 7-plus and their families, and introduce the concert's music in a fun way. Bring along an instrument if you want to play along.

Proms Family Orchestra and Chorus offers everyone – whatever your age or ability – the chance to play and sing alongside professional musicians. See page 83 for how to sign up.

Chekhov's 150th birthday is celebrated on 22 July

The Haberdashers' Aske's Boys' School
Nurturing Excellence

An outstanding independent day school for boys aged between 5 and 18.

Open Day Saturday 9th October 1–4pm
(no appointment necessary)

Headmaster Peter Hamilton MA
Butterfly Lane, Elstree, Hertfordshire WD6 3AF
Tel: 020 8266 1700 office@habsboys.org.uk

www.habsboys.org.uk
registered charity no: 313996

Haberdashers' Aske's School for Girls

Outstanding academic achievement: imagination and creativity

Open Day 9th October 2010
Juniors 10am-12.30pm
Seniors 2pm-5pm

Music Scholarships available at 11+

Independent Day School for Girls from 4-18

Aldenham Road, Elstree, Herts, WD6 3BT
e: admissions@habsgirls.org.uk
t: 020 8266 2338
www.habsgirls.org.uk
Registered Charity No. 313996

CLOCKWISE FROM TOP LEFT: Tansy Davies (8 September), Colin Matthews (28 July), Huw Watkins (17 August) and James Dillon (19 August)

But what if you want to make the music yourself? Bring your instrument and Proms Plus will provide the conductor for six Proms Family Orchestra and Chorus sessions (see page 83 for details of how to sign up). The idea is that you create your own music under the watchful eyes and ears of professional musicians. And, for something a little different, there are two very special *Doctor Who*-themed Proms Family Orchestra and Chorus events on 24 and 25 July.

Putting old and new audiences at ease with a musical repertoire that they may not know was always the ambition behind Family Music Intro workshops, in which players from the orchestra of the evening Prom join an animateur to explain and to explore what they are going to play later. No musical background is required, just listen, learn and enjoy. The appeal of Family Music Intro has been so wide that this season sees the creation of a brand-new series, Music Intro. It's for anyone who wants a door opened to the music, not just families.

And this year Proms Plus has a double plus that's all about Wagner, which is part of a gloriously operatic first weekend at the Royal Albert Hall: Come and Sing Wagner and a special Wagner Study Session on *The Mastersingers of Nuremberg*, both on 17 July (see page 83 for details of how to sign up).

Can't make the trip to South Kensington this year? Don't worry, just ride there on the airwaves. Many of these Proms Plus events are broadcast, usually in the interval of the following concert.

Why do we go to Proms Plus? To face the music with the knowledge that it's ours as much as our neighbours'. See you in the queue outside the Royal College of Music! ●

Christopher Cook broadcasts on BBC Radio 3 and writes for *BBC Music Magazine, Gramophone* and *International Record Review*. He teaches Cultural Studies at the University of Syracuse in London, is a Visiting Professor at the University of the Arts, London, and is Chair of the Cheltenham Music Festival.

For details of all Proms Plus events, please see Listings, pages 110–148

The Royal College of Music, home to Proms Plus

HOW TO PROMS PLUS

- Proms Plus events are free of charge.

- Events are held at the Royal College of Music and (except for the First Night's live *In Tune* event) end one hour before the main evening Prom, allowing you enough time to meet friends or have refreshments before the concert.

- Prommers who have started queuing for the evening's concert ahead of the Proms Plus event can collect a numbered ticket from one of the Royal Albert Hall stewards, enabling them to retain their place in the Prommers' queue. This is especially advisable for the most popular Proms concerts.

- Events are unticketed, except for the First Night's live *In Tune* event (see *page 110*), Proms Family Orchestra and Chorus events (see *page 83*) and Inspire Day on 2 August (see *page 83*), for which free tickets will be issued.

- Please note that seating for all Proms Plus events is unreserved and limited by capacity: we advise arriving early for the more popular events. Doors open 30 minutes before the start-time.

- Since many of the events are recorded for broadcast, latecomers may be admitted only at a suitable break; event stewards will guide you at the appropriate moment.

Stephen Sondheim (31 July) Howard Jacobson (1 August) Anne Fine (31 August) John Suchet (21 July) Sir John Eliot Gardiner (10 Sept)

Talented? Your future is **mado**.

Chetham's School of Music, Manchester

Elmhurst School for Dance, Birmingham

St Mary's Music School, Edinburgh

The Hammond School, Chester

The Purcell School for Young Musicians, Hertfordshire

The Royal Ballet School, London

Tring Park School for the Performing Arts, Hertfordshire

Wells Cathedral School, Somerset

Yehudi Menuhin School, Surrey

- Government funding (up to 100%) available:
    - www.dcsf.gov.uk/mds
    - www.scotland.gov.uk/topics/education/schools/excellence
- Committed to the highest teaching standards in Music & Dance
- Committed to an excellent academic education

www.made-schools.org.uk

THE 9 SCHOOLS OF
MUSIC AND DANCE
EXCELLENCE **mado**

Presenting the Proms

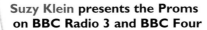

Suzy Klein presents the Proms on BBC Radio 3 and BBC Four
First Proms presentations:
2006 (BBC Television); 2008 (BBC Radio 3)

With the Proms brought to you by BBC Radio 3 – and 25 of them relayed on BBC Television – it's essential to have a team of well-briefed, steely-nerved presenters on hand. Here, four of the voices and faces of the Proms offer their insights into the role, and – in the year that the database of all Proms performances is made available online – they select a Prom from the past for which they would have begged or borrowed a ticket

Many of us have events that mark out the year for us – the school term, religious holidays, family celebrations. For me, the Proms is one of those events.

This festival has been a part of my life for as long as I can remember. I first started going as a teenager, queuing patiently for as many concerts as I could get to, as one of the community of season-ticket Promenaders. After university, I got a job as a researcher in BBC Radio, making features for Proms intervals; I then went on to become a producer, steering the live concerts through their TV broadcasts. Finally, in 2006, I was given the chance to present the Proms on BBC Television. It's been a dream job – how could it be anything else?

I've met and interviewed some outstanding artists: from Sir Peter Maxwell Davies and Valery Gergiev to Anne-Sofie von Otter and Joyce DiDonato. The thrill of live television never quite goes away – nor does the potential for things to go awry. On my first live TV Prom, the conductor was held up backstage by a torn jacket and I was left filling 12 minutes on air (the equivalent of doing Radio 4's *Just a Minute* a dozen times over – no hesitation, repetition or deviation allowed!). On another occasion, we had been on the air only 30 seconds when all the lights in the presentation box failed and I was left broadcasting in the darkness.

Presenting the Proms for radio has the advantage that the audience can't see if anything goes wrong – you can show panic on your face, but certainly not in your voice. Radio and TV both require that you're always on your toes, ready to reflect the particular colour and atmosphere that each concert brings. Relax too much while the music is playing (and that's certainly a seductive option) and you risk not being on top of things when the music stops. So now with the coming of another Proms season I feel, as always, that keen sense of anticipation for another year of the festival that has for so long been part of my life.

Suzy Klein can also be heard on Radio 3's 'Sunday Morning' (Sundays, 10.00am)

Queen's Hall, home of the Proms until 1941

Prom 1 1895

Suzy Klein's pick from the Proms archives …

Saturday 10 August 1895
Queen's Hall

Works by Wagner, Leoncavallo, Chabrier, Chopin (orch. Glazunov), Eckert, Godard, Kenningham, Kistler, Saint-Saëns, Thomas, Gounod, Liszt, Bizet, Rossini, Schubert, Haydn, Mattei, Eilenberg, Mascheroni, Ging'l, Shloesser; plus traditional songs
Soloists, Queen's Hall Orchestra
Henry Wood *conductor*

The first ever Promenade concert isn't necessarily the one I would like to have been at for musical reasons. Certainly, there was a huge choice of repertoire – you could have a bit of Wagner or Bizet, or perhaps some Liszt, Chabrier, Schubert or Haydn. But, given that the concert began at 8.00pm and the programme was monumentally large, it must have been rather a long night at the Queen's Hall.

What the very first Promenade concert does have, though, are the DNA fragments that have gone on to make the festival we know today. As with all Proms seasons since, there was a mix of the great soloists of the day and the best orchestral players. There was also a world premiere that night – by someone called Carl Wilhelm Adolph Schloesser (whom music history seems to have forgotten). Most of all, I would have loved to have shared that evening in the company of Henry Wood, who could never have known that his modest music festival would still be going strong 115 years on. Had he seen the programme for the 2010 Proms season – with its Proms Plus events, countless broadcasts and online presence, available to audiences across the globe – he doubtless would have shaken his head in delighted disbelief.

BBC RADIO 3

90–93FM

THE PROMS ON BBC RADIO 3

- BBC Proms broadcast live on BBC Radio 3 (90–93FM, DAB, digital and online)
- Many Proms repeated during *Afternoon on 3* (weekdays, 2.00pm), plus a series of repeats over the Christmas period
- Listen again for seven days after broadcast via the iPlayer at bbc.co.uk/proms
- Proms-related programmes during the season, including *Breakfast* (daily, 7.00am) and *In Tune* (weekdays, 5.00pm)

Petroc Trelawny **presents the Proms on BBC Radio 3 and BBC Four**

First Proms presentations:
1998 (BBC Radio 3); 2003 (BBC Television)

I know childhood recollections are often rather idealistic, but I'm sure my childhood Proms memories are pretty accurate. At home in Cornwall we had a summer ritual. Supper would be early, and at 7.30pm my mother and I would decamp to the sitting room for the evening's live Prom on Radio 3. She would spin wool or mend clothes, tasks that would not distract from the music – introduced with great authority by announcers such as Tony Scotland or Patricia Hughes. I would have been aged 7 or 8, probably a bit fidgety, but respectful nonetheless of this great event happening in a great hall in the heart of glamorous, buzzing London. The arrival of famous foreign artists would lead to the atlas coming off the shelf; I'd pause and look up from toys or homework as pianist and orchestra united again at the end of a thrilling cadenza.

This is my 13th season as a member of the Radio 3 Proms team and once again this year I'll be presenting the First Night. Although meticulously planned, the 'rig' – the hanging of the microphones and laying of miles of cable – is never actually finished until the very last moment. We'll start to have meetings to discuss scripts and style in May or early June, but it won't be until the rehearsal on the day of the concert that my thoughts will finally be hammered into some sort of narrative that will do justice to the performers and their music. Much of our radio audience will be dipping in and out, hearing a movement or two in the car as they pick up kids or rinse dinner plates. But, as I try to conjure up a radio picture of the Royal Albert Hall and its occupants, in the back of my mind is always an image of my late mother, completely focused on the music – an eager, open-minded child listening by her side.

Petroc Trelawny can also be heard on Radio 3's 'Performance on 3' (weekdays, 7.00pm), 'In Tune' (weekdays, 5.00pm) and 'Music Matters' (Saturdays, 12.15pm)

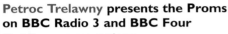

Mstislav Rostropovich in 1964

Prom 30 1968

Petroc Trelawny's pick from the Proms archives …

Wednesday 21 August 1968
Royal Albert Hall

Glinka: Ruslan and Lyudmila – overture
Dvořák: Cello Concerto in B minor
Shostakovich: Symphony No. 10 in E minor
Mstislav Rostropovich *cello*
USSR State Symphony Orchestra
Yevgeny Svetlanov *conductor*

Yevgeny Svetlanov conducting the USSR State Symphony Orchestra in Shostakovich's 10th Symphony makes this occasion pretty irresistible. But it's this concert's place in European history that really makes me wish I'd had a spot in the Arena on that night.

That same day, Wednesday 21 August, Soviet troops occupied Czechoslovakia to crush the Prague Spring. Britain responded cautiously; protestors outside the Royal Albert Hall were less diplomatic, surrounding the building with banners and chants. The Russian orchestra's KGB minders paced nervously backstage – a friend who was there recalled that the players appeared to be terrified – and they performed Glinka's *Ruslan and Lyudmila* overture at a breakneck pace. And then, by apt coincidence, came a Czech masterwork, Dvořák's Cello Concerto, played by Mstislav Rostropovich – who followed it with more Dvořák in his encore. The noisy protests stopped for the music: clear proof of the power of art over conflict.

Katie Derham presents the Proms on BBC Radio 3 and BBC Two

First Proms presentation: 2007 (BBC Television); joins the BBC Radio 3 Proms presentation team this year

Being in the Royal Albert Hall is just the beginning. It has such a special atmosphere: the photos reminding you that you're surrounded by the ghosts of maestros past; the chance that around the next corner you just might bump into a hero, a diva, a star. The sense of theatre, the grandeur of the auditorium, which fills you with excitement even before the first note is played: the knowledge you're about to hear the best musicians in the world performing at the most prestigious celebration of music anywhere – these are the reasons we all love going to the Proms. My job is to communicate that special something to the viewers and listeners at home.

It is, of course, the most enormous privilege. Last year I watched Vasily Petrenko rehearse the National Youth Orchestra of Great Britain: he put those talented young musicians through their paces, but always with the greatest respect, and with good humour. It was thrilling to witness, as it was to hear the fruits of their labours that evening as they performed to a packed and enthusiastic house.

This year – presenting all the Proms broadcast on BBC Two, and many for Radio 3 – I'll get the chance to interview some of my favourite conductors and to spend time with the orchestral players, asking them what makes the Proms so special for them. I want to find out why they love certain pieces and what we at home should be listening out for. There are so many jewels to look forward to, but the Sondheim 80th-birthday concert (Prom 19) will surely be a highlight. Gergiev conducting the World Orchestra for Peace in Mahler's Fourth and Fifth Symphonies (Prom 26) is bound to be an event – and then of course there's Sir Simon Rattle with the Berlin Philharmonic (Prom 66), taking us through a programme including Wagner, Schoenberg and Webern. It will be a chance to listen and enjoy, but also I hope to learn a little, and from the very best in the business. The more I think about it, the luckier I feel. I look forward to joining you for a magical summer.

Katie Derham can also be heard on BBC Radio 3's 'Afternoon on 3' (weekdays, 2.00pm)

Jacqueline Du Pré in 1967

Prom 21 **1962**

Katie Derham's pick from the Proms archives ...

Tuesday 14 August 1962
Royal Albert Hall

Ireland: A London Overture
Delius: Sea Drift
Elgar: Cello Concerto in E minor
Britten: Les illuminations
Walton: Gloria
Jacqueline Du Pré *cello*, Gerald English *tenor*,
Marjorie Thomas *alto*, Ronald Dowd *tenor*,
John Shirley-Quirk *bass-baritone*
London Philharmonic Choir
BBC Singers
BBC Symphony Orchestra
Malcolm Sargent *conductor*

Trying to choose a dream Prom is like getting a bumper box of chocolates – so many choices, so many favourites. My immediate thought was how I wished I'd been at the Prom three years ago, when Gustavo Dudamel introduced us to his phenomenal Simón Bolívar Youth Orchestra of Venezuela (Prom 48, 2007). The colour, the enthusiasm, the fun – it was gripping on television, but to have been there ... wow!

If I had only one journey in my Proms time machine, though, I'd go back to 14 August 1962, when Jacqueline Du Pré gave the first of her four Proms performances of Elgar's Cello Concerto. An iconic musician, playing her signature piece – and one of my all-time favourites. I wore out the tape of her playing this when I was a student, and have always regretted I never heard her live.

Leonard Bernstein in 1987

Charles Hazlewood's pick from the Proms archives ...

Thursday 10 September 1987
Royal Albert Hall

Mozart: Clarinet Concerto in A major
Mahler: Symphony No. 5 in C sharp minor
Peter Schmidl *clarinet*
Vienna Philharmonic Orchestra
Leonard Bernstein *conductor*

This was the first of only two occasions that Leonard Bernstein conducted at the Proms. I can only imagine how fabulously slowly he took the Adagietto in Mahler's Fifth Symphony. He'd have brought out the richness and wonderful lugubriousness of Mahler's music to the full. And he would have revelled in the acoustic of the Hall too – you only need to sneeze in that space and you produce a five-part chord, so think what an impact an epic symphony like this one makes. I can just see him pacing around backstage, chain-smoking beforehand!

Charles Hazlewood **presents the Proms on BBC Four**

First Proms presentations: 1998 (BBC Television); 2002 (BBC Radio 3)

The Proms is a great time of the year for me, because it's practically my only chance to hear other people making music – I'm on the podium the rest of the year. It's also great to be possibly the only person to have regularly conducted and presented at the Proms.

The most important job of the presenter is to get across the energy, excitement and atmosphere in the Hall on any particular night, as that doesn't automatically carry itself into your living room. But it's more than hot air and excitement: we also try to have the kind of discussions that are thought-provoking and engaging enough to make people want to go further into the music, and to explore repertoire that's maybe away from the norm. This year we're focusing ever closer on the music and the artists themselves. I'm excited to be talking – musician to musician – about the quest to find the essence of great music, and the joy of performing it.

I also enjoy the element of multi-tasking required as a presenter.

Interviewing, presenting precise nuggets of information to camera and listening to the producer, all at the same time. You might receive a particular nugget of information through your earpiece while you're talking to a guest, and you have to process this and bring it into conversation at the appropriate moment – it's all part of the fun. I get a real buzz out of that.

I'm one of those people who rise to the challenge when things go off-piste. If you're too tied down to a script, things can become a bit safe and sterile. The broadcast is often better when you're thinking on your feet. Sometimes you find that a guest has slavishly prepared answers in advance, and I like almost to make a point of not asking those questions – the response to more off-beat questions can often be more revealing.

Charles Hazlewood can also be heard on Radio 3's 'Discovering Music' (Sundays, 5.00pm)

THE PROMS ONLINE
bbc.co.uk/proms

- Every Prom available to listen or watch again for seven days after broadcast
- Latest details of daily events at all venues
- Comprehensive programme notes for every concert
- Experience the festival blog – all the latest Proms and Radio 3 angles from the concert venues and behind the scenes
- Daily text alerts to keep you up to date
- Share reviews online or with Radio 3's *Breakfast* (daily, 7.00am) via SMS or email
- Weekly free download, with highlights of Proms interviews from Radio 3's *In Tune* (weekdays, 5.00pm)
- Online Composer Labs for young composers

BBC iPlayer

Proms 2010
Take Your Seats
Inspire 2010
Listen to Radio 3

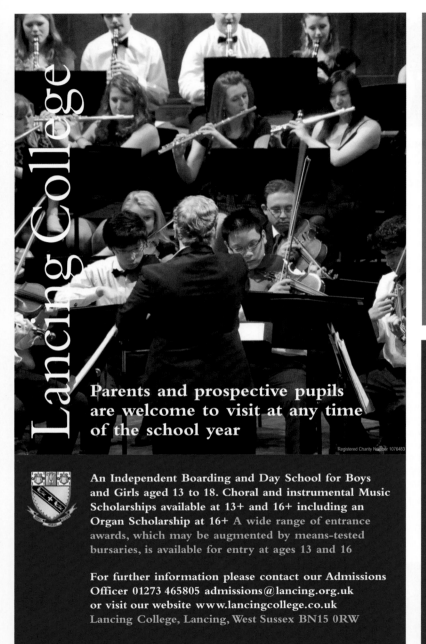

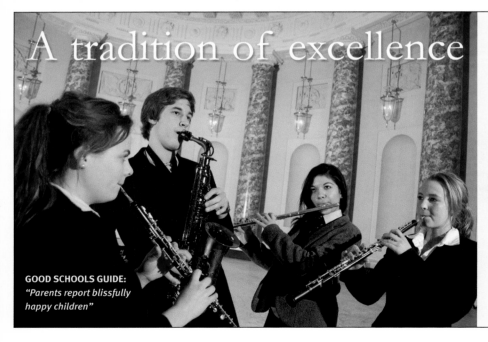

ST PAUL'S
GIRLS' SCHOOL

"Music produces a kind of pleasure
which human nature cannot do withou'
Confucius.

Music scholarships

16+ auditions in November 2010
11+ auditions in January 2011

St Paul's Girls' School is one of the country's leading
independent day schools for girls aged 11-18. The
director of music, Mr Yat-Soon Yeo, is always please
to meet parents of prospective scholars informally
upon request. For details of music scholarship open
events please see the website.

St Paul's Girls' School, Brook Green, London, W6 7E
020 7603 2288 | admissions@spgs.org | www.spgs.c

excellence and innovatio

PIERINO
PASTA PIZZA RESTAURANT
37 THURLOE PLACE, LONDON SW7 2HP

Telephone 020 7581 3770
Monday to Friday 12–3.00pm, 5.30–11.30pm
Saturday & Sunday 12 noon–11.30pm

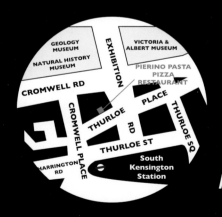

Prompt service guaranteed for you to be in time for the performance.

We are within walking distance of the Royal Albert Hall, near South Kensington tube station.

You are welcome before and after the performance.

EXPERIENCE OF SERVING GENUINE ITALIAN FOOD AND FOR
HOME-MADE PASTA AND THE BEST PIZZA IN LONDON

35 YEARS

Concert Listings

BOOKING

Tickets will go on sale at 8.00am on Tuesday 4 May – online, by telephone and in person. Tickets may also be requested by post.

Plan your Proms concert-going online, before tickets go on sale, by using the new Proms Planner at bbc.co.uk/proms from 12 noon on Thursday 22 April until midnight on Monday 3 May.

Online: bbc.co.uk/proms
Telephone: 0845 401 5040*

For full booking information, see pages 150–160

PRICE CODES

A ▼ **G** Each concert at the Royal Albert Hall falls into one of seven price bands, colour-coded for ease of reference. For a full list of prices, see page 156. For special offers, see page 155.

Please note: *concert start-times vary across the season – check before you book*

All concert details were correct at the time of going to press. The BBC reserves the right to alter artist or programme details as necessary.

The BBC: bringing the Proms to you – in concert, on radio, television and online

WEEKEND PROMMING PASS • BEAT THE QUEUES AND SAVE MONEY (SEE PAGE 155)

FRIDAY 16 JULY

Proms Plus 5.00pm, Royal College of Music

In Tune Sean Rafferty and Petroc Trelawny present a special edition of BBC Radio 3's *In Tune*, featuring Proms artists, music from the season and a preview of the Proms Literary Festival.
Tickets available from BBC Audience Services (bbc.co.uk/tickets)

8.00pm–c9.30pm

Mahler

Symphony No. 8 in E flat major,
'Symphony of a Thousand'   82'

Mardi Byers *soprano*
Twyla Robinson *soprano*
Malin Christensson *soprano*
Stephanie Blythe *mezzo-soprano*
Kelley O'Connor *mezzo-soprano*
Nikolai Schukoff *tenor*
Hanno Müller-Brachmann *baritone*
Tomasz Konieczny *bass*

Choristers of St Paul's Cathedral
Choristers of Westminster Abbey
Choristers of Westminster Cathedral
BBC Symphony Chorus
Crouch End Festival Chorus
Sydney Philharmonia Choirs
BBC Symphony Orchestra
Jiří Bělohlávek *conductor*

Launching our 150th-anniversary celebrations of Mahler's birth, his 'Symphony of a Thousand' begins a weekend-long flourish of three towering works combining voices and orchestra. Setting a hymn to the divine creative spark alongside an exaltation of the feminine spirit from Goethe's *Faust*, Mahler created a work of unprecedented scale and impact. The BBC SO gave its UK premiere 80 years ago under Proms founder-conductor Henry Wood. Tonight's massed choirs lavish on it the force of over 400 adult and children's voices. See 'A View of Eternity', pages 24–31

There will be no interval

Broadcast
RADIO Live on Radio 3
ONLINE Live and 'listen again' options at bbc.co.uk/proms
TV Live on BBC Two

SATURDAY 17 JULY

Proms Plus Royal College of Music

11.00am **Come and Sing Wagner** Join members of Welsh National Opera to sing extracts from Wagner's *The Mastersingers of Nuremberg*. For ages 16-plus. *See page 83 for details of how to sign up.*

11.00am **Wagner Study Session** Join John Deathridge and Tim Blanning to explore *The Mastersingers of Nuremberg*. *See page 83 for details of how to sign up.*

2.15pm **Proms Intro** Louise Fryer introduces *The Mastersingers of Nuremberg* with Patrick Carnegy, author of *Wagner and the Art of the Theatre*, and Anthony Negus of WNO's music staff.
Edited version broadcast on Radio 3 during tonight's first interval

4.00pm–c10.15pm

Wagner

The Mastersingers of Nuremberg   270'
(concert staging; sung in German)

Bryn Terfel *Hans Sachs*
Raymond Very *Walther von Stolzing*
Amanda Roocroft *Eva*
Christopher Purves *Beckmesser*
Andrew Tortise *David*
Anna Burford *Magdalene*
David Soar *Nightwatchman*
Brindley Sherratt *Pogner*
Simon Thorpe *Kothner*
David Stout *Nachtigall*
Paul Hodges *Schwarz*
Rhys Meirion *Zorn*
Andrew Rees *Eisslinger*
Stephen Rooke *Moser*
Arwel Huw Morgan *Foltz*
Geraint Dodd *Vogelgesang*
Owen Webb *Ortel*

**Chorus and Orchestra
of Welsh National Opera**
Lothar Koenigs *conductor*

Wagner's story of the young outsider Walther who wins Nuremberg's time-honoured song contest – and the bride of his dreams – brings Bryn Terfel to the role of the forward-looking cobbler-poet Hans Sachs for the first time. See 'Arias and Graces', pages 18–21

There will be two intervals, of 25 and 60 minutes

PROM 2
Spotlight on … Bryn Terfel

It was 21 years ago that Welsh bass-baritone Bryn Terfel sprang to fame, while still a student, singing an aria from Wagner's *The Flying Dutchman* in the final of the Cardiff Singer of the World competition. A year later he made his stage debut with Welsh National Opera and soon after built up a hugely successful international operatic career.

With this Welsh National Opera production of Wagner's monumental *The Mastersingers of Nuremberg*, Terfel makes his debut in the role of Hans Sachs – 'a daunting prospect,' he has admitted. 'I had the score on my piano for a whole year and, when you open that first page, you know you're going to find Hans Sachs on every page, in every scene, for five hours.'

And the rehearsal period is testing too. 'With Mozart you have a social life: you can go out with colleagues, to restaurants, to the movies. But when you are performing Wagner, your social life disappears: you have to be much more careful to preserve your stamina.'

Broadcast
RADIO Live on Radio 3
ONLINE Live and 'listen again' options at bbc.co.uk/proms
TV Broadcast on BBC Four at 7.00pm

Booking opens 8.00am on 4 May: online at bbc.co.uk/proms • by telephone 0845 401 5040* • in person at the Royal Albert Hall

Prom 3

SUNDAY 18 JULY

Proms Plus 4.15pm, Royal College of Music
Proms Intro Louise Fryer introduces Verdi's *Simon Boccanegra* in conversation with musicologists Alexandra Wilson and Roger Parker.
Edited version broadcast on Radio 3 during tonight's interval

6.00pm–c9.00pm

Verdi

Simon Boccanegra (1881 version)   134'
(semi-staged; sung in Italian)

Plácido Domingo *Simon Boccanegra*
Marina Poplavskaya *Amelia*
Joseph Calleja *Gabriele Adorno*
Ferruccio Furlanetto *Jacopo Fiesco*
Jonathan Summers *Paolo Albiani*
Lukas Jakobski *Pietro*

Royal Opera Chorus
Orchestra of the Royal Opera House
Antonio Pappano *conductor*

In the course of his long operatic career Plácido Domingo has performed over 130 tenor roles, excelling in a vast range of repertoire. Following his Proms debut – only five years ago – in the Royal Opera's production of Wagner's *Die Walküre*, he returns with the company in a new departure: his much-anticipated first role as a baritone, for which he is taking on one of Verdi's greatest characters, Simon Boccanegra – the Doge-to-be at the centre of intrigue and uprising among the rulers and people of Venice. Antonio Pappano conducts a starry cast in this costumed semi-staging. See 'Arias and Graces', pages 18–21

There will be one interval

Plácido Domingo

Broadcast
RADIO Live on Radio 3
ONLINE Live and 'listen again' options at bbc.co.uk/proms

Proms Chamber Music 1

MONDAY 19 JULY

1.00pm–c2.00pm

Proms Chamber Music at Cadogan Hall

Schubert

Die Forelle, D550	2'
Des Fischers Liebesglück, D933	7'
Vor meiner Wiege, D927	6'
Die Sterne, D939	4'
Three Piano Pieces, D946 – No. 3 in C major	5'

Schumann

Dichterliebe, Op. 48   30'

Mark Padmore *tenor*
Imogen Cooper *piano*

Mark Padmore   Imogen Cooper

Our Schumann bicentenary celebrations begin with the composer at his most intimate and poignant. The 16 Heine settings of *Dichterliebe* ('A Poet's Love') trace a poet's increasing dejection as he reflects upon his imagined love. One of Britain's foremost tenors features as its protagonist – partnered by leading pianist Imogen Cooper, who joins Padmore in a sequence of Schubert songs, and performs a lively Schubert miniature. See 'A Mind Unhinged …?', pages 34–37

There will be no interval

Broadcast
RADIO Live on Radio 3
ONLINE Live and 'listen again' options at bbc.co.uk/proms

Prom 4

MONDAY 19 JULY

Proms Plus 5.45pm, Royal College of Music
Proms Literary Festival Mad, bad and dangerous to know? Lord Byron, Romantic poet and creator of *Manfred*, is discussed by poet and critic Tom Paulin and writer of the BBC drama *Byron*, Nick Dear. Matthew Sweet hosts.
Edited version broadcast on Radio 3 during tonight's interval

7.30pm–c9.50pm

Schumann, orch. Mahler
Manfred – overture   13'

Rachmaninov
Piano Concerto No. 2 in C minor   35'

interval

Tchaikovsky
Manfred   55'

Simon Trpčeski *piano*

Royal Liverpool Philharmonic Orchestra
Vasily Petrenko *conductor*

As the moody Romantic hero *par excellence*, Byron's Manfred appealed to artists across the board. While the brooding overture of Schumann's incidental music captures the tale's supernatural Alpine setting, Tchaikovsky's response is a fusion of tone-poem and Classical form whose full-length portrait of the protagonist stands as one of its composer's greatest achievements. Brilliant Macedonian pianist Simon Trpčeski, a graduate of BBC Radio 3's New Generation Artists scheme, joins the Royal Liverpool Philharmonic under its trailblazing Principal Conductor Vasily Petrenko. See 'A View of Eternity', pages 24–31; 'A Mind Unhinged …?', pages 34–37

Simon Trpčeski

Broadcast
RADIO Live on Radio 3
ONLINE Live and 'listen again' options at bbc.co.uk/proms
TV Recorded for broadcast on BBC Two on 24 July

TUESDAY 20 JULY

Proms Plus 5.45pm, Royal College of Music
Proms Intro Martin Handley talks to the WDR Symphony Orchestra's General Manager, Siegwald Bütow, and Principal Cellist, Oren Shevlin, about the orchestra and tonight's programme.

7.30pm–c10.10pm

Wagner
Lohengrin – Prelude (Act 1)   9'

Mendelssohn
Violin Concerto in E minor, Op. 64   28'

Gunther Schuller
Where the Word Ends   25'
UK premiere

interval

R. Strauss
An Alpine Symphony   50'

Viviane Hagner *violin*

WDR Symphony Orchestra, Cologne
Semyon Bychkov *conductor*

Viviane Hagner

The WDR Symphony Orchestra, Cologne – the first of the season's visiting international orchestras – includes music by three of its compatriots. The sustained stillness of the Prelude to Wagner's *Lohengrin* (whose Act 3 Prelude appears in Prom 72) begins at the opposite extreme to the raging torrents and vivid mountain imagery conjured up in Strauss's epic tone-poem. Following her Proms debut in 2007, Munich-born Viviane Hagner returns as soloist in Mendelssohn's popular Violin Concerto, and the first premiere of the season comes from American Gunther Schuller, 85 this year – an equally celebrated figure in the big-band jazz and classical music worlds. *See 'New Music', pages 52–59*

Broadcast
RADIO Live on Radio 3
ONLINE Live and 'listen again' options at bbc.co.uk/proms

WEDNESDAY 21 JULY

Proms Plus 5.15pm, Royal College of Music
Proms Intro Broadcaster and Beethoven biographer John Suchet, in discussion with Petroc Trelawny, explores the man behind the music. Actor Paul Rhys, star of BBC Two's three-part drama-documentary *Beethoven* (2005), brings the composer to life.
Edited version broadcast on Radio 3 during tonight's interval

7.00pm–c9.05pm

Beethoven
Overture 'Egmont'   9'

Piano Concerto No. 1 in C major   38'

interval

The Creatures of Prometheus – overture   5'

Piano Concerto No. 4 in G major   33'

Paul Lewis *piano*

BBC Symphony Orchestra
Jiří Bělohlávek *conductor*

One of today's leading Beethoven interpreters, Paul Lewis begins his cycle of all five piano concertos, partnered tonight by the orchestra and conductor with whom he recently recorded them. The First and Fourth concertos contrast Beethoven's early rhythmic drive with later introspective insight, while two overtures convey the drama of Goethe's heroic Egmont, killed for railing against political oppression, and of Prometheus's Creatures, formed with the help of fire from the gods. The BBC Symphony Orchestra and Chief Conductor Jiří Bělohlávek revive the time-honoured tradition of Beethoven Nights at the Proms (*see also Prom 14*). See 'The Spirit of Beethoven', pages 40–43

Paul Lewis

PROM 6
Spotlight on ... Jiří Bělohlávek

As the BBC Symphony Orchestra's Chief Conductor, Jiří Bělohlávek is no stranger to the Proms, this year conducting four concerts, including the First and Last Nights. Those two appearances alone present the contrasting challenges of Mahler's monumental 'Symphony of a Thousand' and the wide-ranging musical celebration (not to mention the traditional speech-giving) of the Last Night. While in his next appearance this summer (Prom 72) Bělohlávek takes on a programme spanning Wagner and Bruckner to Tansy Davies (the latter a BBC commission), tonight sees an all-Beethoven programme and a continuation of the conductor's recent recording project with Paul Lewis, covering the complete Beethoven piano concertos. 'The pleasure I had in collaborating with Paul Lewis on our recording project reinforced the decision to bring us together on this occasion. By the time of this Prom, we will have finished the recordings. That was our first artistic collaboration, and I hope that many more will follow. He is an extraordinary pianist – his instrumental ability is breathtaking.'

SAME-DAY SAVER
Book for both Proms 6 and 7 and save (see page 155)

Broadcast
RADIO Live on Radio 3
ONLINE Live and 'listen again' options at bbc.co.uk/proms
TV Recorded for broadcast on BBC Four on 23 July at 7.30pm

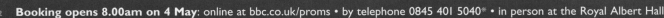

WEDNESDAY 21 JULY

10.00pm–c11.15pm

Chopin

Nocturnes – selection   c60'

Maria João Pires piano

The magical atmosphere of the Royal Albert Hall can be at its most potent in intimate performances. In the bicentenary year of Chopin's birth, this aspect of the Hall becomes central to this Late Night Prom, which celebrates the artistry of Portuguese pianist Maria João Pires, whose 2008 recording of Chopin's *Nocturnes* drew wide acclaim.

There will be no interval

SAME-DAY SAVER
Book for both Proms 6 and 7 and save (see page 155)

PROM 7
Spotlight on ... Maria João Pires

It's more than a decade since Portuguese pianist Maria João Pires made her acclaimed recording of Chopin's *Nocturnes*, and in this bicentenary year of the composer's birth she has released a new CD of his late works – which reached No. 6 in the pop charts of her native Portugal.

Chopin forms a cornerstone of Pires's repertoire, as he does for most pianists, but familiarity doesn't bring complacence: 'It is still always a challenge to produce the sound that comes as close as possible to the feelings you have for the music.' Her warm tone and her affection for these 'miniatures' – 'not a pejorative word,' she emphasises – would seem especially appropriate for their often languorous mood. 'These pieces show an incredible direct connection to the source of music. There are composers who have to construct their music; however, the *Nocturnes* are about fluidity between music and the composer himself. This is what we call inspiration.'

Famously shy of large venues, Chopin would have feared playing in the spacious setting of the Royal Albert Hall. Will this be a challenge to Pires? 'I will imagine that I am in a small, intimate hall with 100 people. Imagination is important in life.'

Broadcast
RADIO Live on Radio 3
ONLINE Live and 'listen again' options at bbc.co.uk/proms

THURSDAY 22 JULY

Proms Plus 5.45pm, Royal College of Music
Proms Literary Festival Creator of TV drama *Our Friends in the North*, Peter Flannery, and Russian specialist Rosamund Bartlett celebrate the life and work of Anton Chekhov, 150 years after his birth – with readings by actor Romola Garai.
Edited version broadcast on Radio 3 during tonight's interval

7.30pm–c10.00pm

Britten

Sinfonia da Requiem   21'

Prokofiev

Piano Concerto No. 1 in D flat major   15'

interval

Shostakovich

Symphony No. 7 in C major, 'Leningrad'   75'

Alexander Toradze piano

BBC National Orchestra of Wales
Thierry Fischer conductor

Wartime music dominates the season's first visit by the BBC National Orchestra of Wales, tonight under its Principal Conductor since 2006, Thierry Fischer. Britten's early orchestral masterpiece, inspired by three sections of the Christian Mass for the dead, was a product of his years in the USA but reflects the mood of Europe in 1941. Shostakovich completed his graphic Seventh Symphony the same year, as Leningrad – the city of his birth – lay under German siege. By contrast, Prokofiev's witty and exuberant student Piano Concerto displays the optimism of a young composer (and a formidable pianist) at the beginning of his career.

Thierry Fischer

Broadcast
RADIO Live on Radio 3
ONLINE Live and 'listen again' options at bbc.co.uk/proms
TV Live on BBC Four

WEEKEND PROMMING PASS • BEAT THE QUEUES AND SAVE MONEY (SEE PAGE 155)

FRIDAY 23 JULY

Proms Plus 5.30pm, Royal College of Music
Family Music Intro Rachel Leach and members of the
BBC Philharmonic offer a family introduction to tonight's concert.
Bring your instrument and join in!

7.30pm–c9.45pm

Parry
Symphonic Fantasia in B minor, '1912'
(Symphony No. 5)   25'

Scriabin
Piano Concerto in F sharp minor   28'

interval

Tchaikovsky
Symphony No. 6 in B minor, 'Pathétique'   46'

Nelson Goerner *piano*

BBC Philharmonic
Vassily Sinaisky *conductor*

'Stress', 'Love', 'Play', 'Now!'. The movement titles of
Parry's last symphony hint at hidden autobiographical
significance, and celebrate a composer rarely noticed
beyond the Last Night (*see also Proms 31 and 68*).
It is paired with the most famous autobiographical
symphony of all, Tchaikovsky's heroic attempt to
outrun and finally confront despair. At the centre of
the BBC Philharmonic's first appearance this season
is the early, Chopin-tinged piano concerto by another
great Russian (whose works we feature this season),
with much-admired Argentinian soloist Nelson
Goerner. *See 'Coloured Ambition', pages 46–49*

Nelson Goerner

PROM 9
Spotlight on ... Vassily Sinaisky

During his 14 years as the BBC Philharmonic's
Principal (now Chief) Guest Conductor, Vassily
Sinaisky has won renown for his interpretations
of the Russian classics. But along the way he has
become a champion of the English repertoire too.
Aptly, his Prom draws these two passions together.

The popularity of Tchaikovsky's rousing
swansong, the 'Pathétique' Symphony, has not
diminished its expressive power, though Sinaisky
admits, 'Even though it is my favourite piece, I try
not to conduct it too much, as every performance
of it should be a special event.'

Scriabin was a composer who, in his time,
was as feted as Rachmaninov, but his orchestral
works have come to be neglected. 'Scriabin's
concerto is a wonderful, fascinating piece,' believes
Sinaisky. 'It has such lightness of texture and
beautiful melodies – especially for the clarinet,
one of Scriabin's favourite instruments.'

Sinaisky also leads the debut Proms
performance of Parry's *Symphonic Fantasia*.
'The richness and breadth of English music is
something that I never fully appreciated before I
got to know it through my collaboration with the
BBC Philharmonic – it has been a true journey of
discovery for me. Now I love to introduce these
masterpieces to new audiences when I conduct
orchestras throughout the world.'

Broadcast
RADIO Live on Radio 3
ONLINE Live and 'listen again' options at bbc.co.uk/proms

SATURDAY 24 JULY

Proms Plus Royal College of Music
2.00pm Proms Family Orchestra and Chorus You know
how the theme tune to *Doctor Who* goes, now come and play it!
See page 83 for details of how to sign up.
5.45pm Proms Intro Join members of the *Doctor Who* sound
design team to discover how they create the stunning sound-
scapes for the BBC TV series. Presented by Matthew Sweet.

7.30pm–c9.30pm

Doctor Who Prom

Programme to include:

Murray Gold
Music from the *Doctor Who* series*   c40'

John Adams
Short Ride in a Fast Machine   5'

Holst
The Planets – Mars   6'

Orff
Carmina burana – 'O Fortuna'   5'

Wagner
Die Walküre – The Ride of the Valkyries   5'

Karen Gillan *host*
Matt Smith *host*

London Philharmonic Choir
BBC National Orchestra of Wales
***Ben Foster** conductor*
Grant Llewellyn *conductor*

Karen Gillan (companion Amy Pond) and Matt Smith
(the Doctor) host an intergalactic musical adventure
featuring Murray Gold's music from the TV series,
plus a selection of classical favourites. *See 'Deep
Impact', pages 78–79*

There will be one interval

Broadcast
RADIO Live on Radio 3
ONLINE Live and 'listen again' options at bbc.co.uk/proms
TV Recorded for future broadcast on BBC Three

SUNDAY 25 JULY

11.00am–c1.00pm

Doctor Who Prom

Karen Gillan host
Matt Smith host

London Philharmonic Choir
BBC National Orchestra of Wales
Ben Foster conductor
Grant Llewellyn conductor

There will be one interval

For programme details, see Prom 10

SAME-DAY SAVER
Book for both Proms 11 and 12 and save (see page 155)

SUNDAY 25 JULY

Proms Plus Royal College of Music
1.45pm **Proms Family Orchestra and Chorus** You know how the theme tune to *Doctor Who* goes, now come and play it! *See page 83 for details on how to sign up.*
4.45pm **Proms Intro** To celebrate the 200th anniversary of Schumann's birth, pianist Lucy Parham talks to Sara Mohr-Pietsch about his life and works, with readings from Robert and Clara Schumann's diaries.
Edited version broadcast on Radio 3 during tonight's interval

6.30pm–c8.40pm

Schumann

Overture, Scherzo and Finale, Op. 52	18'
Piano Concerto in A minor	30'

interval

J. Strauss II

Die Fledermaus – overture	8'
Where the Lemon Trees Blossom – waltz	8'
Thunder and Lightning – polka	3'
Emperor Waltz	11'
By the Beautiful Blue Danube – waltz	9'

J. Strauss I

Radetzky March	3'

Christian Zacharias piano

BBC Philharmonic
Sir Charles Mackerras conductor

Sir Charles Mackerras revives the spirit of the Proms Viennese Night, once an annual fixture, with a variety of fleet-footed Strauss-family classics. In the first half, the accent is German rather than Austrian, continuing the season's Schumann bicentenary celebrations. Here, the probing and sensitive Christian Zacharias is the soloist in Schumann's Piano Concerto, whose finale contains a buoyant waltz. See 'A Mind Unhinged …?', pages 34–37

PROM 12
Spotlight on … Christian Zacharias

Christian Zacharias performed Schumann's Piano Concerto at his most recent Proms appearance in 2004. On that occasion he also directed the Lausanne Chamber Orchestra (of which he is Artistic Director), adding the task of conducting to the already challenging piano part. This year he leaves the orchestra in the capable hands of Sir Charles Mackerras, with whom he has performed the work a number of times.

'Schumann, of course, is not easy,' says Zacharias, who has a range of Schumann's solo piano works under his belt. 'He has rhythmically intricate ideas which suggest one thing but which actually hide another.' He mentions in particular the 'hidden waltz' of the finale – not actually notated as a simple waltz, but which comes to sound that way through a kind of aural *trompe l'oeil*.

Has Zacharias's parallel career as a conductor affected the way he approaches his piano playing? 'I tend now to see a piece more from the wider, symphonic standpoint, so that, even if I'm the pianist, the structure still seems strong: I have to be part of a bigger image. Often the problem with soloists is that they can get lost in the detail, and conductors don't like that too much!'

Broadcast
RADIO Live on Radio 3
ONLINE Live and 'listen again' options at bbc.co.uk/proms

MONDAY 26 JULY

1.00pm–c2.00pm

Proms Chamber Music at Cadogan Hall

Debussy
Préludes – selection   10'

Jouni Kaipainen
String Quartet No. 6   c12'
BBC co-commission with the
Royal Philharmonic Society: world premiere

Schumann
Piano Quintet in E flat major, Op. 44   30'

Francesco Piemontesi *piano*
Meta4

The young Finnish string quartet Meta4 and Francesco Piemontesi – both Radio 3 New Generation Artists – join forces in Schumann's Piano Quintet, beloved by performers and listeners alike for its melodic sweep and passionate momentum. The recital begins with a selection of Debussy's evocative piano miniatures and the quartet introduces a specially commissioned work by its compatriot Jouni Kaipainen, one of the astonishing generation of composers nurtured in Finland over the last half-century. *See 'A Mind Unhinged …?', pages 34–37; 'New Music', pages 52–59*

There will be no interval

Meta4

Broadcast
RADIO Live on Radio 3
ONLINE Live and 'listen again' options at bbc.co.uk/proms

MONDAY 26 JULY

Proms Plus 5.15pm, Royal College of Music
Proms Intro Simon Holt talks about his role as Composer-in-Association with the BBC National Orchestra of Wales, and is joined by percussionist Colin Currie to discuss his percussion concerto, *a table of noises*, performed in tonight's Prom. Presented by Tom Service.

7.00pm–c9.05pm

Cherubini
Médée – overture   8'

Schumann
Symphony No. 1 in B flat major, 'Spring'   32'

interval

Simon Holt
a table of noises   29'
London premiere

R. Strauss
Till Eulenspiegels lustige Streiche   15'

Colin Currie *percussion*
BBC National Orchestra of Wales
Thierry Fischer *conductor*

The BBC National Orchestra of Wales launches our cycle of Schumann symphonies with the First, whose freshness and drive reflect the productive frenzy that seized the composer around the time of his marriage. It's preceded by the stirring overture to the Cherubini opera which Brahms hailed as 'the highest peak of dramatic music'. Written for tonight's soloist, Simon Holt's percussion concerto was partly inspired by the table of tools kept by his great-uncle, a taxidermist. The perky adventures of Strauss's mythical rogue form a brilliantly coloured conclusion. *See 'A Mind Unhinged …?', pages 34–37; 'New Music', pages 52–59*

PROM 13
Spotlight on … Colin Currie

'Very intimate, very tender, very moving' – not a description you'd give to every percussion concerto, but one that Colin Currie applies to *a table of noises*. 'Simon [Holt] took the idea of the percussion concerto and stood it on its head. He's approached it with the idea that small is beautiful. There are moments of intense virtuosity, but most of the time my job is more to take care of balance and texture, as if being part of a chamber ensemble. It's a very well-rounded and beautiful piece of music.'

After Currie asked Holt for a new work, the composer visited the percussionist at home to look at the cornucopia of instruments available to him. 'He was attracted by the more delicate sounds,' says Currie, 'one of which was the Peruvian *mesa de ruidos*', or 'table of noises', which gave the piece its title – indeed most of the percussion instruments used are laid out on a single table.

The cavernous Royal Albert Hall will present an acoustical challenge, but one that Currie is eager to turn to his advantage: 'One of the things about the Hall is that soft sounds can carry very well, if you take a little bit of care. I've got to hold the audience's attention as closely as possible: if everyone is listening, then there's no problem.'

Broadcast
RADIO Live on Radio 3
ONLINE Live and 'listen again' options at bbc.co.uk/proms

TUESDAY 27 JULY

Proms Plus 5.45pm, Royal College of Music
Proms Literary Festival Phil Grabsky, director of *In Search of Beethoven*, and historian Tim Blanning discuss whether Beethoven truly embodies the spirit of the tortured Romantic artist. Actor Paul Rhys, star of BBC Two's three-part drama-documentary *Beethoven* (2005), brings the composer to life.
Edited version broadcast on Radio 3 during tonight's interval

7.30pm–c9.55pm

Beethoven

| Symphony No. 1 in C major | 26' |
| Violin Concerto in D major | 45' |

interval

| Symphony No. 5 in C minor | 33' |

Hilary Hahn *violin*

Deutsche Kammerphilharmonie Bremen
Paavo Järvi *conductor*

Hilary Hahn

In the second of this season's two Beethoven Nights, the airy First Symphony and the rousing Fifth frame the expansive Violin Concerto – of which tonight's American soloist, Hilary Hahn, made a Grammy Award-winning recording at the age of 18. Returning for only its third appearance at the Proms, the Deutsche Kammerphilharmonie Bremen gives its first performance here under its Artistic Director, Paavo Järvi.

Broadcast
RADIO Live on Radio 3
ONLINE Live and 'listen again' options at bbc.co.uk/proms

WEDNESDAY 28 JULY

Proms Plus 5.45pm, Royal College of Music
Proms Composer Portrait Colin Matthews, in conversation with Tom Service, introduces a selection of his chamber works: *Chaconne with Chorale and Moto perpetuo, Scorrevole, Calmo, Duo No. 3, Enigma No. 1* and his arrangement of Britten's *Sonnet*. Performed by musicians from the Royal Academy of Music.
Edited version broadcast on Radio 3 following tonight's Prom

7.30pm–c10.05pm

Stockhausen

| Jubilee | 16' |

interval

Sir Harrison Birtwistle

| Sonance Severance 2000 | 3' |

Colin Matthews

| Violin Concerto | 20' |
London premiere

Luke Bedford

| Outblaze the Sky | 6' |

interval

Zimmermann

| Rheinische Kirmestänze | 6' |

Schumann

| Symphony No. 3 in E flat major, 'Rhenish' | 33' |

Leila Josefowicz *violin*

BBC Symphony Orchestra
Oliver Knussen *conductor*

Continuing our Schumann symphony cycle in the bicentenary of the composer's birth, the Third is the most pictorial, evoking by turns a beer garden by the Rhine and the Gothic magnificence of Cologne Cathedral. A century later came Bernd Alois Zimmermann's witty *Rhine-Church Festival Dances*, celebrating the same German region. Stockhausen's festive overture from 1977 opens the programme, which also features a trio of recent British works.
See 'A Mind Unhinged …?', pages 34–37; 'New Music', pages 52–59.

PROM 15
Spotlight on … Leila Josefowicz

'Every soloist has to be realistic about their strengths,' says the pragmatic Canadian violinist Leila Josefowicz, 'because there are a lot of us out there. Twenty-first-century music is my passion, and it's something I think I can do very well.' It's this dedication to contemporary music that won her the multi-disciplinary MacArthur Foundation Fellowship, often nicknamed the 'genius award'.

It's no wonder, then, that Colin Matthews wrote his latest concerto for her. 'Contemporary music is my speciality, so I'll cheekily say that I think he made the right decision!' Not every new work is right for her – she tends to avoid meticulously written pieces that leave no room for personal input. 'I like pieces that are artfully crafted, yet need a strong interpretation. I need lyricism in whatever kind of music I play, with contrasts of mood and texture. It's got to be memorable.'

Matthews's piece ticks every box on her wish list. 'The structure of the piece is very unusual, very memorable. It starts in a song-like way, and unfolds in a very improvisatory manner. By the end the suspense that has built up is explosive. It's a wonderful, deep and mysterious work.'

Broadcast
RADIO Live on Radio 3
ONLINE Live and 'listen again' options at bbc.co.uk/proms

THURSDAY 29 JULY

Proms Plus 5.00pm, Royal College of Music
Family Music Intro Explore the music of tonight's three great composers with conductor (and mentor from the BBC's *Maestro* series) Matthew Rowe. Bring your instrument to play along with musicians from the City of Birmingham Symphony Orchestra.

7.00pm–c9.05pm

Wagner
Rienzi – overture   12'

Beethoven
Piano Concerto No. 2 in B flat major   30'

interval

Dvořák
Symphony No. 9 in E minor,
'From the New World'   45'

Paul Lewis piano

City of Birmingham Symphony Orchestra
Andris Nelsons conductor

The vigorous overture from Wagner's early, rarely staged epic set in medieval Rome opened the very first Prom 115 years ago. Here it raises the curtain on the second instalment of Paul Lewis's Beethoven piano concerto cycle – an infectiously lively adventure beyond the boundaries of Mozart into a style that was Beethoven's own. This visit by Birmingham's orchestra and its dynamic Latvian Music Director ends with

Andris Nelsons

Dvořák's musical response to the period he spent in America, during which he helped establish an American musical identity, much as he had developed a nationalist school in his Czech homeland. See 'The Spirit of Beethoven', pages 40–43

Broadcast
RADIO Live on Radio 3
ONLINE Live and 'listen again' options at bbc.co.uk/proms
TV Broadcast on BBC Four at 7.30pm

THURSDAY 29 JULY

10.00pm–c11.30pm

Dvořák
Serenade in D minor for winds, cello and double bass, Op. 44   25'

Mozart
Serenade in B flat major, K361 'Gran Partita'   50'

Scottish Chamber Orchestra
Sir Charles Mackerras conductor

Sir Charles Mackerras

Celebrating his 85th birthday this year, Sir Charles Mackerras presides over a late-night pairing of two composers who conjured luscious sounds for wind ensembles, and (as one of the leading interpreters of Czech music) teases out a Dvořák thread following the symphony of this evening's earlier Prom. Sir Charles directs members of the Scottish Chamber Orchestra – of which he is now Conductor Laureate, having served as Principal Guest Conductor from 1992 to 1995. His long association with the ensemble has produced acclaimed recordings of repertoire from Mozart operas to Brahms symphonies.

SAME-DAY SAVER Book for both Proms 16 and 17 and save (see page 155)

There will be no interval

Broadcast
RADIO Live on Radio 3
ONLINE Live and 'listen again' options at bbc.co.uk/proms

WEEKEND PROMMING PASS (SEE PAGE 155)

FRIDAY 30 JULY

Proms Plus 5.45pm, Royal College of Music
Music Intro An illustrated guide to the Proms and the music in tonight's concert, with Fraser Trainer and members of The Australian Youth Orchestra – ideal for anyone exploring classical music for the first time.

7.30pm–c9.35pm

Brett Dean
Amphitheatre   10'
London premiere

Mahler
Des Knaben Wunderhorn – selection   23'

interval

Shostakovich
Symphony No. 10 in E minor   50'

Ekaterina Gubanova mezzo-soprano

The Australian Youth Orchestra
Sir Mark Elder conductor

Sir Mark Elder, who returns next week with his Hallé orchestra, here introduces the first of the summer's youth orchestras. In his 10th Symphony Shostakovich embedded motto themes relating both to himself and to the young woman with whom he was infatuated, while for Mahler the German folk-poetry collection *Des Knaben Wunderhorn* ('The Youth's Magic Horn') proved a rich source of inspiration. Australian composer (and former Berlin Philharmonic viola player) Brett Dean based his orchestral fantasy on the description in a German children's book of a ruined Roman amphitheatre. See 'A View of Eternity', pages 24–31; 'New Music', pages 52–59

Broadcast
RADIO Live on Radio 3
ONLINE Live and 'listen again' options at bbc.co.uk/proms
TV Live on BBC Four

SATURDAY 31 JULY

Proms Plus Royal College of Music
1.00pm **Proms Family Orchestra and Chorus**
A Sondheim-themed Family Orchestra and Chorus session.
See page 83 for details of how to sign up.
5.45pm **Proms Intro** Join the celebrations to mark Stephen Sondheim's 80th birthday as he discusses tonight's works with David Charles Abell. Presented by Petroc Trelawny.
Edited version broadcast on Radio 3 during tonight's interval

7.30pm–c9.30pm

Sondheim at 80

Cast to include:

Bryn Terfel *bass-baritone*
Maria Friedman *vocalist*
Simon Russell Beale *vocalist*

**Singers from the
BBC Performing Arts Fund
BBC Concert Orchestra
David Charles Abell** *conductor*
Martin Duncan *director*

David Charles Abell

Marking the 80th birthday of one of Broadway's great innovators, this first ever all-Sondheim Prom draws together leading figures of the opera and theatre worlds, plus some further special guests. Bryn Terfel – a magnetic Sweeney Todd, as he proved at the Royal Festival Hall in 2007 – leads a starry cast, joined by aspiring young performers supported by the BBC Performing Arts Fund. On the bill are excerpts from the horror-opera *Sweeney Todd*, the Ingmar Bergman-inspired *A Little Night Music* and the fairy-tale compendium of *Into the Woods*, as well as excerpts from *Company*, *Pacific Overtures* and *Sunday in the Park with George*. For another Broadway event, see Prom 49.
See 'Bring on Broadway', pages 72–75

There will be one interval

Broadcast
RADIO Live on Radio 3
ONLINE Live and 'listen again' options at bbc.co.uk/proms
TV Broadcast on BBC Two at 8.00pm

SUNDAY 1 AUGUST

4.00pm–c5.00pm

Wagner, arr. Lemare
The Mastersingers of Nuremberg – overture   12'

Tannhäuser – overture   14'

**Improvisation on themes from
Wagner's 'Tristan and Isolde'**   15'

Wagner, arr. Lemare
Die Walküre – The Ride of the Valkyries   6'

Wayne Marshall *organ*

Picking up on the opening weekend's complete performance of *The Mastersingers of Nuremberg* and a number of other Wagner works during the season, charismatic organist Wayne Marshall turns a vividly coloured spotlight on the composer. The grandeur of the two opera overtures translates fittingly to the Royal Albert Hall's mighty instrument, while the airborne Valkyries may need to hold on to their horses even more tightly than usual during this particular flight. As one of the most fluent and ingenious of keyboard improvisers, Marshall turns his attention to *Tristan and Isolde* – forming an upbeat to tonight's performance of the opera's second act.

There will be no interval

Wayne Marshall

SAME-DAY SAVER Book for both Proms 20 and 21 and save (see page 155)

Broadcast
RADIO Live on Radio 3
ONLINE Live and 'listen again' options at bbc.co.uk/proms

SUNDAY 1 AUGUST

Proms Plus 4.45pm, Royal College of Music
Proms Literary Festival *The History of Love* Novelist Howard Jacobson and Classics scholar Mary Beard chart the inspirational influence of famous lovers, from Tristan and Isolde to Romeo and Juliet. Rana Mitter hosts.
Edited version broadcast on Radio 3 during tonight's interval

6.30pm–c8.30pm

Berlioz
Romeo and Juliet – Love Scene   18'

interval

Wagner
Tristan and Isolde – Act 2   70'
(concert performance; sung in German)

Violeta Urmana *Isolde*
Ben Heppner *Tristan*
Franz-Josef Selig *King Mark*
Sarah Connolly *Brangäne*
Timothy Robinson *Melot*
Henk Neven *Kurwenal*

**Orchestra of the Age
of Enlightenment
Sir Simon Rattle** *conductor*

Violeta Urmana

In the first of his three appearances this season, Sir Simon Rattle evokes two pairs of history's most symbolic lovers – contrasting Berlioz's response to Shakespeare with Wagner's to a medieval Celtic legend (the latter featuring two of today's leading Wagner singers, Ben Heppner and Violeta Urmana). Rattle has a long-standing relationship with the Orchestra of the Age of Enlightenment, and together they offer a chance to hear two great Romantic scores performed on instruments of the period.
See 'Arias and Graces', pages 18–21

Ben Heppner

Broadcast
RADIO Live on Radio 3
ONLINE Live and 'listen again' options at bbc.co.uk/proms

MONDAY 2 AUGUST

1.00pm–c2.00pm

Proms Chamber Music at Cadogan Hall

Brahms
Four Heine settings: Es liebt sich so lieblich im Lenze!, Op. 71 No. 1; Sommerabend, Op. 85 No. 1; Mondenschein, Op. 85 No. 2; Meerfahrt, Op. 96 No. 4   12'

Berg
Seven Early Songs   15'

Wolf
Italienisches Liederbuch – selection   23'

Malin Christensson soprano
Henk Neven baritone
Hans Eijsackers piano

Following the Schumann and Schubert songs of the first Proms Chamber Music recital, today's performers extend the *Lieder* repertoire towards three of its finest later exponents and celebrate the 150th anniversary of the birth of Hugo Wolf. Brahms and Wolf broadened the art-song's range respectively towards dark-hued introspection and characterful vignettes, whereas Berg's expansive melodies touch on a heady post-Romantic atmosphere. Henk Neven returns after last night's Wagner, joined by fellow Radio 3 New Generation Artist Malin Christensson and young Dutch pianist Hans Eijsackers.

There will be no interval

Malin Christensson   Henk Neven   Hans Eijsackers

Broadcast
RADIO Live on Radio 3
ONLINE Live and 'listen again' options at bbc.co.uk/proms

MONDAY 2 AUGUST

> **Proms Plus** 5.30, Royal College of Music
> **Proms Inspire Day** The Aurora Orchestra, conducted by Nicholas Collon, performs the winning entries from this year's Proms Inspire Young Composers' Competition. Presented by Sara Mohr-Pietsch. *(Reduced seating capacity)*
> Edited version broadcast on Radio 3 following Prom 27 on 6 August

7.30pm–c9.35pm

Mozart
Piano Concerto No. 27 in B flat major, K595   30'

Ligeti
Musica ricercata – No. 2: Mesto, rigido e ceremoniale   3'

George Benjamin
Duet   12'
London premiere

interval

Ravel
Valses nobles et sentimentales   17'

Miroirs – Une barque sur l'océan   8'

La valse   12'

Pierre-Laurent Aimard piano

BBC Symphony Orchestra
Jonathan Nott conductor

Pierre-Laurent Aimard

Echoing the waltzes of last month's Viennese Night (Prom 12), tonight's Prom ends with a trio of Ravel pieces in which an evocative waterscape is framed by contrasting evocations of the waltz – one celebrating Vienna's heyday, the other casting a wry backwards glance over its decline. Two contrasting piano concertos – a first by George Benjamin (50 this year) and Mozart's last – display the wide-ranging talents of pianist Pierre-Laurent Aimard, a friend and colleague of Benjamin since they met as students of Olivier Messiaen in Paris. Given its UK premiere at last year's Aldeburgh Festival, where Aimard is Artistic Director, *Duet* is a search for sounds that orchestra and piano can share. See 'New Music', pages 52–59

PROM 22
Spotlight on ... Jonathan Nott

'A really good programme, for me, has a journey. For this concert, we knew we wanted to perform George Benjamin's *Duet*. It has a lot of light and shade, darkness as well as dance elements. Also, in its play of seemingly one melodic line between the piano and orchestra, it's not a typical concerto.

'The clean, almost stark way the notes are put together reminded me of the ceremonial aspect of the second piece from Ligeti's *Musica ricercata* for solo piano, and then came the idea of making the whole evening a paean to piano music – with this Ligeti piece for piano alone, the Benjamin and Mozart for piano with orchestra, and then the three Ravel orchestral pieces – two of which were originally composed for solo piano.

'There's light and darkness in the second half too. In *Valses nobles* there's an endless pleasure in completely inconsequential pursuits – a throwing-awayness of life. It's one of the most deftly put-together whiling-aways of time that I know. And though you have seductive charm and perfume in *La valse* as well, there's also a life force so strong it's almost destructive – a supreme energy of creation coupled with a destructive power that is just hovering around the corner.'

Broadcast
RADIO Live on Radio 3
ONLINE Live and 'listen again' options at bbc.co.uk/proms

Prom 23

TUESDAY 3 AUGUST

Proms Plus 5.45pm, Royal College of Music
Proms Literary Festival *Samuel Pepys Anniversary* Journalist and author Max Hastings and historian Jenny Uglow join Ian McMillan to mark 350 years since Samuel Pepys began the most influential diary in British history.
Edited version broadcast on Radio 3 during tonight's interval

7.30pm–c10.00pm

Foulds
Dynamic Triptych   26'

Vaughan Williams
Serenade to Music   11'

interval

Vaughan Williams
The Lark Ascending   14'

Elgar
Symphony No. 1 in A flat major   53'

Elin Pritchard, Marie Claire Breen, Emily Mitchell, Natalie Montakhab *sopranos*
Jemma Brown, Beth Mackay, Rebecca Afonwy-Jones, Lynda-Jane Workman *mezzo-sopranos*
Stephen Chambers, Warren Gillespie, John Pumphrey, Ronan Busfield *tenors*
James Birchall, Owain Browne, Michel de Souza, Ross McInroy *basses*
Ashley Wass *piano*
Nicola Benedetti *violin*

BBC Scottish Symphony Orchestra
Donald Runnicles *conductor*

Donald Runnicles makes his first Proms appearance as Chief Conductor of tonight's orchestra in an all-British programme featuring former BBC Young Musician of the Year Nicola Benedetti in her Proms debut. Proms founder-conductor Henry Wood gave the world premiere of *Serenade to Music* at his Jubilee Concert in 1938; tonight's singers are from the Royal Scottish Academy of Music and Drama.

Broadcast
RADIO Live on Radio 3
ONLINE Live and 'listen again' options at bbc.co.uk/proms

Prom 24

WEDNESDAY 4 AUGUST

Proms Plus 5.15pm, Royal College of Music
Music Intro Matthew Rowe and members of the BBC Scottish Symphony Orchestra introduce Mahler's epic Third Symphony. Whether it's your first time at the Proms or you're a regular, this event will offer an imaginative insight into tonight's Prom.

7.00pm–c8.50pm

Mahler
Symphony No. 3 in D minor   100'

Karen Cargill *mezzo-soprano*

Edinburgh Festival Chorus (women's voices)
Royal Scottish National Orchestra Junior Chorus
BBC Scottish Symphony Orchestra
Donald Runnicles *conductor*

Karen Cargill   Donald Runnicles

Continuing our Mahler anniversary celebration – and bringing the first of a trio of his symphonies on two consecutive nights – Donald Runnicles conducts Mahler's massive Third Symphony, the most rousing and touching of his early efforts to encapsulate the whole world within a single work. Its visions of verdant nature and heavenly love sprang from the composer's intention to give 'the whole of nature a voice'. See 'A View of Eternity', pages 24–31

There will be no interval

Broadcast
RADIO Live on Radio 3
ONLINE Live and 'listen again' options at bbc.co.uk/proms
TV Recorded for broadcast on BBC Four on 5 August at 7.30pm

Prom 25

WEDNESDAY 4 AUGUST

10.00pm–c11.10pm

Bach
Canonic Variations on 'Vom Himmel hoch', BWV 769   11'

Bach, arr. Stravinsky
Chorale Variations on 'Vom Himmel hoch', BWV 769   12'

Stravinsky
Threni   35'

Elizabeth Atherton *soprano*
Hilary Summers *mezzo-soprano*
Alan Oke *tenor*
Andrew Kennedy *tenor*
David Wilson-Johnson *baritone*
Sir John Tomlinson *bass*
Daniel Hyde *organ*

BBC Singers
London Sinfonietta
David Atherton *conductor*

The London Sinfonietta's Late Night Prom reunites the orchestra with its founder-conductor David Atherton. The two Stravinsky works were premiered in Venice during the 1950s and share the haunting, distilled musical language that the ever-evolving composer adopted in later

Sir John Tomlinson

years. *Threni*, receiving its first Proms performance, sets the Lamentations of Jeremiah in a quirky and intensely spiritual style, while Stravinsky's recasting of Bach's variations on the Christmas hymn 'Vom Himmel hoch' embellishes them in ever-changing instrumental colours. The original variations for organ open the programme.

SAME-DAY SAVER Book for both Proms 24 and 25 and save (see page 155)

There will be no interval

Broadcast
RADIO Live on Radio 3
ONLINE Live and 'listen again' options at bbc.co.uk/proms

THURSDAY 5 AUGUST

Proms Plus 5.45pm, Royal College of Music
Proms Intro Valery Gergiev and Charles Kaye (co-founder and Director of the World Orchestra for Peace), along with World Orchestra for Peace musicians Edward Vanderspar (Principal Viola, London Symphony Orchestra) and George Vosburgh (Principal Trumpet, Pittsburgh Symphony Orchestra), in conversation with Proms Director Roger Wright.

7.30pm–c10.10pm

Mahler
Symphony No. 4 in G major   56'

interval

Mahler
Symphony No. 5 in C sharp minor   70'

Camilla Tilling soprano

World Orchestra for Peace
Valery Gergiev conductor

Camilla Tilling

In the first of his two appearances this season (see *Prom 41*) Valery Gergiev – who led a memorable Mahler cycle with the London Symphony Orchestra in 2007/8 – conducts a highlight of our celebrations marking the composer's 150th anniversary. Making its third Proms visit, the World Orchestra for Peace was conceived by Georg Solti as an assembly of first-rate players from around the world to promote peace. Mahler's Fourth Symphony continues the idealistic vision of its predecessor, performed last night, while the Fifth is an all-too-human journey through storm and stress, enshrining his love for his wife Alma in the heartrending Adagietto, and propelling glimpses of glory towards a stirring finale. See *'A View of Eternity'*, pages 24–31

PROM 26
Spotlight on … Valery Gergiev

Many know and love the tireless Valery Gergiev for his work with the Mariinsky Theatre in St Petersburg, the London Symphony Orchestra and the Metropolitan Opera, New York. But in addition to these roles and his guest conducting engagements, he is also Conductor of the World Orchestra for Peace – founded by Georg Solti in 1995 from hand-picked players around the world 'to demonstrate unmistakably the unique strength of music as an ambassador for peace in our time'.

Solti only had the opportunity to conduct a single concert with his orchestra before his death in 1997, whereupon Gergiev took over the reins. But Solti still remains firmly in Gergiev's memory: 'I admired his electrifying way of making great music; he combined huge personal authority with fiery – in the warmest sense – leadership. From this came the respect and admiration of both musicians and his audiences.' Nor has he lost sight of Solti's original aims. 'Of course we cannot stop a war but, if just one politician is moved to see and hear so many nations communicating in such harmony, then we will help in a small way to make the world a more peaceful one for our children.'

Broadcast
RADIO Live on Radio 3
ONLINE Live and 'listen again' options at bbc.co.uk/proms
TV Recorded for broadcast on 7 August. Symphony No. 5 will be shown on BBC Two; Symphony No. 4 will be available via the red button.

FRIDAY 6 AUGUST

Proms Plus 5.15pm, Royal College of Music
Music Intro Matthew Rowe and musicians from the Hallé bring tonight's concert to life by uncovering the stories behind the pieces. Live musical examples and jargon-free explanations make this perfect for first-time concert-goers!

7.00pm–c9.10pm

Foulds
April – England, Op. 48 No. 1   8'

Beethoven
Piano Concerto No. 3 in C minor   36'

interval

R. Strauss
Ein Heldenleben   50'

Paul Lewis piano

Hallé
Sir Mark Elder conductor

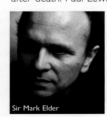
Sir Mark Elder

Sir Mark Elder returns with the Hallé (of which he has been Music Director since 2000) for one of the great late-Romantic orchestral showpieces. In *Ein Heldenleben* ('A Hero's Life') Strauss cast himself as the central composer-hero – castigated by critics, reassured by his wife and rising above adversity to become exalted after death. Paul Lewis reaches the intense No. 3 in his Beethoven concerto voyage, and a second John Foulds piece (see *Prom 23*) shows this Mancunian – the son of a Hallé orchestra bassoonist – celebrating the English springtime. See *'The Spirit of Beethoven'*, pages 40–43

SAME-DAY SAVER
Book for both Proms 27 and 28 and save (see page 155)

Broadcast
RADIO Live on Radio 3
ONLINE Live and 'listen again' options at bbc.co.uk/proms
TV Broadcast on BBC Four at 7.30pm

FRIDAY 6 AUGUST

10.15pm–c11.30pm

Oliver Knussen
Two Organa   *6'*

Hans Abrahamsen
Wald   *18'*
BBC co-commission with Asko|Schönberg:
UK premiere

Luke Bedford
Or voit tout en aventure   *15'*

George Benjamin
Three Inventions for Chamber Orchestra   *17'*

Claire Booth soprano

Birmingham Contemporary Music Group
George Benjamin conductor

Claire Booth

In his 50th-birthday year, George Benjamin directs one of the UK's foremost new music ensembles. Alternating between the sensuous and the punchy, the programme sets British composers Knussen and Bedford, as well as Benjamin's own work, alongside the UK premiere of Hans Abrahamsen's *Wald*, which seeks to combine simplicity and poetry. See 'New Music', pages 52–59

There will be no interval

SAME-DAY SAVER
Book for both Proms 27 and 28 and save (see page 155)

PROM 28
Spotlight on … George Benjamin

At the age of only 20, composer George Benjamin made his Proms debut with his *Ringed by the Flat Horizon*, a piece of such maturity that it returned to the Proms two seasons ago. 'I had been coming to the Proms regularly since my childhood,' Benjamin recalls, 'and so it was quite simply a dream come true. It was unquestionably a seminal moment in my life as a musician.'

Now 50, and a seasoned conductor as well as a renowned composer, he conducts his *Three Inventions for Chamber Orchestra*, alongside pieces by three composers he particularly admires. 'Oliver Knussen and I have been close friends since the late 1970s, and I have always revered his talents, both as composer and conductor. The definition and finesse of Luke Bedford's music has impressed me greatly, in particular this haunting and evocative song-cycle based on medieval French poetry. Hans Abrahamsen was part of the strong generation of Scandinavian composers who came to prominence in the 1980s. His recent evolution has been simply extraordinary; no other contemporary composer interests me more, and it's a privilege to present a new work of his this year at the Proms.'

Broadcast
RADIO Live on Radio 3
ONLINE Live and 'listen again' options at bbc.co.uk/proms

SATURDAY 7 AUGUST

Proms Plus 5.45pm, Royal College of Music
Proms Intro NYO musicians and composers offer an insight into their fantasy-themed Prom, with performances of works by NYO composers and new pieces from a special afternoon workshop held by RCM Sparks (see page 85). Presented by Petroc Trelawny in discussion with workshop leader Brian Irvine.
Recorded for future broadcast on Radio 3

7.30pm–c9.30pm

Dukas
The Sorcerer's Apprentice   *11'*

Julian Anderson
Fantasias   *25'*
London premiere

interval

Berlioz
Symphonie fantastique   *50'*

National Youth Orchestra of Great Britain
Semyon Bychkov conductor

The National Youth Orchestra's annual Prom brings two of the greatest feats of 19th-century French orchestration: Paul Dukas's thrilling mix of witty narrative and symphonic momentum and the symphony that made the young Hector Berlioz's name, with its nightmarish  Semyon Bychkov storyline. The orchestra's summer programme also includes the London premiere of Julian Anderson's capricious, contrast-packed showcase for each orchestral section in turn. See 'New Music', pages 52–59

Broadcast
RADIO Live on Radio 3
ONLINE Live and 'listen again' options at bbc.co.uk/proms
TV Recorded for broadcast on BBC Two on 21 August

WEEKEND PROMMING PASS • BEAT THE QUEUES AND SAVE MONEY (SEE PAGE 155)

SUNDAY 8 AUGUST

4.00pm–c5.30pm

Daniel-Lesur
Le cantique des cantiques — 20'

Takemitsu
Garden Rain* — 8'

Stephen Montague
Wilful Chants — c16'
BBC commission: world premiere

Takemitsu
Signals from Heaven* — 6'

Poulenc
Figure humaine — 19'

BBC Symphony Chorus
Soloists from Trinity College of Music
Chamber Choir
London Brass
O Duo
Stephen Jackson conductor
***Andrew Crowley** conductor

The BBC Symphony Chorus – one of Europe's leading large choirs – takes the spotlight in this afternoon Prom, under its Director of 21 years, Stephen Jackson. While Daniel-Lesur's *The Song of Songs* sets biblical eroticism in the sensuous French tradition, Stephen Montague in his new commission is inspired partly by the rhythmic play of linguistic utterance for its own sake. In two hushed, hypnotic brass pieces, Takemitsu, like his 'great mentor' Debussy, makes his visions unfold with dream-like spontaneity. By contrast, Poulenc's wartime cantata from occupied France – one of the great challenges of the choral repertoire – moves from despair to hope in a hymn to freedom. See 'New Music', pages 52–59

There will be no interval

Broadcast
RADIO Live on Radio 3
ONLINE Live and 'listen again' options at bbc.co.uk/proms

SUNDAY 8 AUGUST

Proms Plus 5.45pm, Royal College of Music
Proms Intro Professor of Music Jeremy Dibble (Durham University) and Parry's great-granddaughter, Laura Ponsonby, discuss the life and works of the composer and former Director of the Royal College of Music. Martin Handley presents.

7.30pm–c9.50pm

Messiaen
Un sourire — 10'

Mozart
Piano Concerto No. 17 in G major, K453 — 30'

interval

Parry
Elegy for Brahms — 14'

Brahms
Symphony No. 4 in E minor — 45'

Louis Lortie piano

BBC Symphony Orchestra
Sir Andrew Davis conductor

Sir Andrew Davis

The BBC Symphony Orchestra's Conductor Laureate, Sir Andrew Davis, conducts a typically wide-ranging programme whose pairings reflect two musical homages. According to Messiaen, 'Mozart always smiled. His music also smiled.' Hence the title of the French composer's tribute, written for the Mozart bicentenary in 1991. Parry's elegy to Brahms, whom he regarded as 'the last of the great German heroes of musical art', precedes Brahms's Fourth Symphony, whose final-movement Passacaglia influenced Parry's 'English' Symphony.

SAME-DAY SAVER Book for both Proms 30 and 31 and save (see page 155)

Broadcast
RADIO Live on Radio 3
ONLINE Live and 'listen again' options at bbc.co.uk/proms

MONDAY 9 AUGUST

1.00pm–c2.00pm

Proms Chamber Music at Cadogan Hall

J. S. Bach
Trio Sonata in G major, BWV 1038 — 8'

W. F. Bach
Flute Sonata in E minor, BR B17 — 12'

C. P. E. Bach
Trio Sonata in C major, W149 — 12'

W. F. Bach
Keyboard Fantasia in E minor, BR A24 — 8'

J. S. Bach
Musical Offering – Trio Sonata — 13'

Musica ad Rhenum
Jed Wentz flute/director

Musica ad Rhenum

As a prelude to Bach Day (Saturday 14 August), the Amsterdam-based ensemble Musica ad Rhenum plays music by the figurehead of this extraordinary musical dynasty and two of his composer sons. Two works honour the 300th anniversary of Wilhelm Friedemann Bach; and there are trio sonatas by his younger brother Carl Philipp Emanuel and by their father Johann Sebastian. The concert culminates in Johann Sebastian's great trio sonata from the *Musical Offering*, his collection of canons, fugues and other pieces based on a theme by Frederick II of Prussia.

There will be no interval

Broadcast
RADIO Live on Radio 3
ONLINE Live and 'listen again' options at bbc.co.uk/proms

MONDAY 9 AUGUST

Proms Plus 5.15pm, Royal College of Music
Proms Literary Festival Tom Holland, novelist and award-winning historian of *Rubicon*, and Anne Janowitz, Professor of Poetry, explore the Romantic hero of Lord Byron's narrative poem *Childe Harold's Pilgrimage*. Matthew Sweet hosts.
Edited version broadcast on Radio 3 during tonight's interval

7.00pm–c9.00pm

Tchaikovsky
Fantasy Overture 'Romeo and Juliet'   20'

Janáček
Taras Bulba   24'

interval

Berlioz
Harold in Italy   42'

Maxim Rysanov *viola*

European Union Youth Orchestra
Sir Colin Davis *conductor*

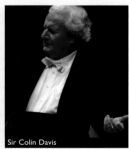
Sir Colin Davis

The third youth orchestra of the season brings the fruits of its summer residency with Sir Colin Davis. One of the world's great Berlioz champions, Davis includes the composer's evocation of Byron's hero Childe Harold, whose solo viola part was written for Paganini and is performed here by former Radio 3 New Generation Artist Maxim Rysanov (who returns on the Last Night). Further colourful orchestral narratives come in Janáček's explosive tone-poem – honouring a Cossack hero – and in the family feuding (as well as the rapt love music) of Tchaikovsky's Shakespearean fantasy.

SAME-DAY SAVER Book for both Proms 32 and 33 and save (see page 155)

Broadcast
RADIO Live on Radio 3
ONLINE Live and 'listen again' options at bbc.co.uk/proms

MONDAY 9 AUGUST

10.00pm–c11.20pm

BBC Radio 3
World Routes Academy

Ilham Al Madfai *guitar/vocalist*
Khyam Allami *oud*

Saro Kevorkian *drum kit*
Anwar Abo Daoud *joza*
Faisal Ghazi *percussion*
Omar Ahmed Majeed *percussion*
Suhad Najm Abdullah *qanun*
Nicola Barakat *electric bass*
Robert Michel *guitar*

Pioneering Iraqi guitarist, singer and composer Ilham Al Madfai was the first in his country to internationalise Iraqi music and blend it with contemporary world styles. He brings a group of musicians to present his own songs as well as arrangements of Iraqi standards, and he introduces young oud player Khyam Allami, whom he has been mentoring as part of BBC Radio 3's new World Routes Academy. Damascus-born, London-resident Allami came to the oud – the Middle Eastern lute – via the violin, drums and bass guitar. He is the first recipient of this exciting scholarship, founded to foster artistic collaborations and support young artists working in world music.

There will be no interval

Ilham Al Madfai

PROM 33
Spotlight on … Khyam Allami

Though only in his late twenties, Khyam Allami has already travelled a rich musical journey. Born in Syria to Iraqi parents, he was brought up in London from the age of 9. In his teens, after learning the violin, he turned to the drums and electric bass, playing in rock bands. Around seven years later something still seemed missing. 'I had quite a good rhythmic understanding and could express myself well, but I felt limited in terms of melody.' Allami began listening again to the songs he had heard while growing up in Syria, as well as to Indian music, and here he found his road to Damascus. 'While listening, all of a sudden I'd hear just one note that totally fired me up and I'd be baffled at how that could be so important.' He soon came to a realisation: 'It's not that note, it's what's around it and how you're getting it. Once you start getting into the details of non-Western music, you start to find the secrets of why it makes such an emotional impact. Drawn to the oud (Arabic lute) partly as a way back to his Iraqi heritage, Allami has also studied North Indian and Azerbaijani music. The first student of Radio 3's World Routes Academy, his preparations for tonight's Prom with mentor Ilham Al Madfai included shadowing the master – the first musician to mix Iraqi and Western influences – over a three-week period of concerts and collaborations in Beirut, Damascus and Amman.

Broadcast
RADIO Live on Radio 3
ONLINE Live and 'listen again' options at bbc.co.uk/proms

TUESDAY 10 AUGUST

Proms Plus 5.30pm, Royal College of Music
Family Music Intro Join Rachel Leach and members of tonight's visiting orchestra as they bring alive this evening's programme with stories behind the music, participation and live examples. Bring your instrument along and join in.

7.30pm–c10.10pm

Schreker
Der ferne Klang – Nachtstück   *16'*

Korngold
Violin Concerto   *25'*

interval

Mahler
Symphony No. 7   *80'*

Leonidas Kavakos *violin*

Deutsches Symphonie-Orchester Berlin
Ingo Metzmacher *conductor*

Ingo Metzmacher

Two key figures of Austria's flourishing early-20th-century opera scene open tonight's Prom. Pronounced a genius by Mahler at the age of 9, Erich Korngold showed a prodigious gift for melody that later bore fruit in his Hollywood film scores, which he happily plundered for his Violin Concerto. The 'Nocturne' of Schreker's operatic dream sequence – portraying the sleepless night of the opera's composer-hero Fritz – finds a counterpart in the two 'Night Music' movements of Mahler's Symphony No. 7. Ingo Metzmacher returns to the Proms after conducting Messiaen's epic opera *Saint Francis of Assisi* in 2008 to great critical acclaim. *See 'A View of Eternity', pages 24–31*

Broadcast
RADIO Live on Radio 3
ONLINE Live and 'listen again' options at bbc.co.uk/proms

WEDNESDAY 11 AUGUST

Proms Plus 5.15pm, Royal College of Music
Proms Intro Andrew McGregor is joined by musicians from the Danish National Symphony Orchestra and its General Manager Ole Bækhøj to discuss music-making in Denmark and the orchestra's new home, the DR Concert Hall.

7.00pm–c10.05pm

Ligeti
Night   *3'*
Morning   *2'*

Tchaikovsky
Violin Concerto   *35'*

interval

Ligeti
Lux aeterna   *9'*

Langgaard
Music of the Spheres   *36'*
UK premiere

interval

Sibelius
Symphony No. 5 in E flat major   *32'*

Inger Dam-Jensen *soprano*
Henning Kraggerud *violin*

Danish National Vocal Ensemble
Danish National Concert Choir
Danish National Symphony Orchestra
Thomas Dausgaard *conductor*

Thomas Dausgaard conducts his Danish forces in Tchaikovsky's ever-captivating Violin Concerto and Sibelius's Fifth Symphony, overwhelming in its nobly expansive final-movement 'Swan Hymn' climax. Three short choral pieces by György Ligeti – including *Lux aeterna*, heard in Stanley Kubrick's *2001: A Space Odyssey* – take us to ethereal heights, while Ligeti himself recognised the mesmeric, free-floating character of Rued Langgaard's 1918 *Music of the Spheres* as prefiguring his own style. *See 'New Music', pages 52–59*

PROM 35
Spotlight on ... Thomas Dausgaard

'I feel very privileged visiting the Proms with both "my" orchestras this year; this programme with the Danish National Symphony Orchestra, one of the leading exponents of Nordic music, and a second visit with the Swedish Chamber Orchestra (Prom 51). This is a programme of associations: my compatriot Langgaard's *Music of the Spheres* was written at exactly the same time as Sibelius was completing his Fifth Symphony and, to keep these company, I have chosen two of their musical "friends": Ligeti – who called himself a Langgaard imitator, and Tchaikovsky, whom Sibelius admired.

'*Music of the Spheres* is written for large orchestra, including organ and piano (brushing the strings rather than using the keys!), choir plus a small distant orchestra with a soprano soloist – eminently suited to the Royal Albert Hall, I think! Motifs, musical styles, repetitions, instruments and registers are used symbolically, drawing us into a world of conflict between evil and good, between "anti-music" and heavenly music – truly music of the spheres! In Ligeti's music I hear the same timelessness, dimensional layering, static repetitions, cinematic changes and colours, completely in contrast to the Sibelius, which develops organically.'

Broadcast
RADIO Live on Radio 3
ONLINE Live and 'listen again' options at bbc.co.uk/proms

THURSDAY 12 AUGUST

Proms Plus 5.45pm, Royal College of Music
Music Intro Rachel Leach offers a jargon-free guide to tonight's Prom, with live musical examples from members of the BBC Symphony Orchestra.

7.30pm–c9.35pm

Berlioz
Overture 'Le corsaire'   9'

Chopin
Piano Concerto No. 2 in F minor   31'

interval

Roussel
Symphony No. 3   25'

Ravel
Daphnis and Chloë – Suite No. 2   18'

Nelson Freire piano

BBC Symphony Orchestra
Lionel Bringuier conductor

Lionel Bringuier

Berlioz's exuberant portrait of seafaring brigands launches an evening of colourful virtuosity with Lionel Bringuier – the young Frenchman already established as Associate Conductor of the Los Angeles Philharmonic, who tonight makes his Proms debut. Renowned Chopin interpreter Nelson Freire marks the composer's bicentenary, and the concert ends with the joyous final scenes from Ravel's lavishly scored pastoral ballet set in Ancient Greece. Roussel's vivid, action-packed Third Symphony is one of the finest flowerings of the French symphonic tradition that began with Saint-Saëns and Franck.

PROM 36
Spotlight on ... Nelson Freire

'I have a long and beautiful history with Chopin's F minor Concerto. I fell in love with it when I was 14, after I discovered the recording of it by my fellow Brazilian pianist Guiomar Novaes, with Otto Klemperer and the Vienna Symphony Orchestra. I heard it, and had a crush!

'When I went to study in Vienna, my teacher Bruno Seidlhofer gave a masterclass in which I played the work for the first time. I had just befriended Martha Argerich and I asked her to play the orchestral reduction for me in the class. As usual, she modestly said, "Oh no, it's too difficult!" and so on. But she did, and I was so proud she accompanied me in front of all those students.

'I've noticed that, when I'm about to play this work I practise it much more than other concertos – maybe because it's so difficult, but also because it's such a pleasure to work on. People say Chopin's orchestration is poor, but I must admit that whenever I hear the orchestral introduction, I am as touched as when I hear Beethoven or Brahms.

'There are a few great conductors who love the F minor Concerto but, unfortunately, I think they are the minority. I always ask a conductor if they love it before agreeing to play it – if not, I prefer not to do it. It's so beautiful, it should not be spoilt.'

Broadcast
RADIO Live on Radio 3
ONLINE Live and 'listen again' options at bbc.co.uk/proms

Prom 37

Seats
£7 to £35

PRICE
BAND **A**

WEEKEND PROMMING PASS (SEE PAGE 155)

FRIDAY 13 AUGUST

Proms Plus 5.45pm, Royal College of Music
Music Intro Matthew Rowe and musicians from the BBC Philharmonic bring tonight's concert to life. Live musical examples and a simple guide through the programme make this perfect for first-time concert-goers!

7.30pm–c9.35pm

Verdi
La forza del destino – overture   8'

Dallapiccola
Partita   27'

interval

Bruch
Violin Concerto No. 1 in G minor   25'

Schumann
Symphony No. 4 in D minor (1851 version)   38'

Sarah Tynan soprano
James Ehnes violin

BBC Philharmonic
Gianandrea Noseda conductor

Sarah Tynan

The BBC Philharmonic returns with Chief Conductor Gianandrea Noseda to contrast the music of Italy and Germany. Canadian violinist James Ehnes, who has recorded all three of Bruch's violin concertos, is the soloist in the composer's most enduring contribution to the repertoire, and Sarah Tynan appears in the concluding lullaby to the Blessed Virgin Mary of Luigi Dallapiccola's ambitious *Partita*, the work which established the composer's international reputation. Schumann's Fourth Symphony, continuing our complete cycle in the bicentenary of the composer's birth, constitutes one of the most exhilarating works in the Romantic repertoire.
See 'A Mind Unhinged ...?', pages 34–37

Broadcast
RADIO Live on Radio 3
ONLINE Live and 'listen again' options at bbc.co.uk/proms
TV Live on BBC Four

SATURDAY 14 AUGUST • BACH DAY

11.30am–c12.40pm

Proms Saturday Matinee at Cadogan Hall

J. S. Bach

Brandenburg Concerto No. 1 in F major*	20'
Brandenburg Concerto No. 6 in B flat major	18'
Brandenburg Concerto No. 4 in G major*	16'

English Baroque Soloists
***Sir John Eliot Gardiner** conductor*

Following our day-long celebration of the great 'J. S.' in 2008, we return to expose further layers of the composer's enduring genius. The first two concerts of this year's Bach Day bring the complete Brandenburg Concertos, performed by the English Baroque Soloists under the guidance of Sir John Eliot Gardiner. 'No other set of concertos,' maintains Gardiner, 'can compare with Bach's for diversity of instrumental make-up, for the prominence and variety of wind instruments, or for the myriad textural contrasts that this allows.' *See 'Bach Bites', pages 68–69*

There will be no interval

Broadcast
RADIO Live on Radio 3
ONLINE Live and 'listen again' options at bbc.co.uk/proms

1.30pm–c2.40pm

Proms Saturday Matinee at Cadogan Hall

J. S. Bach

Brandenburg Concerto No. 3 in G major	15'
Brandenburg Concerto No. 5 in D major	22'
Brandenburg Concerto No. 2 in F major*	12'

English Baroque Soloists
***Sir John Eliot Gardiner** conductor*

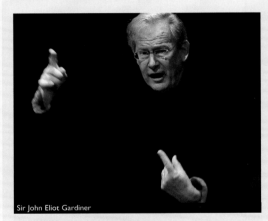

Sir John Eliot Gardiner

The English Baroque Soloists and Sir John Eliot Gardiner continue Bach Day with the second instalment of the complete Brandenburg Concertos. At the centre is No. 5, with its elaborate cadenza for solo harpsichord; No. 3 uses its resources of 10 solo strings to devise ever-changing textures, dancing rhythms and sonorous harmonies; and No. 2 has a dazzling, notoriously challenging trumpet part that exploits the very top of the instrument's range. *See 'Bach Bites', pages 68–69*

There will be no interval

Broadcast
RADIO Live on Radio 3
ONLINE Live and 'listen again' options at bbc.co.uk/proms
TV Part recorded for broadcast later the same day on BBC Two

Proms Plus 3.30pm, Royal College of Music
Proms Intro The conductor of tonight's concert (Prom 39), Andrew Litton, celebrates Bach Day with composers Tarik O'Regan and Alissa Firsova, who discuss Bach and the treatment of his music. Presented by Sara Mohr-Pietsch.
Edited version broadcast on Radio 3 during the interval of Prom 39

5.00pm–c6.00pm

J. S. Bach

Passacaglia and Fugue in C minor, BWV 582	14'
Chorale Prelude 'Wachet auf, ruft uns die Stimme', BWV 645	5'

J. S. Bach, arr. Stainton B. Taylor

Cantata No. 208 – Aria 'Schafe können sicher weiden'	5'

J. S. Bach, arr. Virgil Fox

Chorale 'Komm, süsser Tod', BWV 478	6'

J. S. Bach, arr. David Briggs

Orchestral Suite No. 3 in D major	21'

David Briggs *organ*

Bach Day moves on to the Royal Albert Hall for its third concert, as David Briggs, Organist Emeritus at Gloucester Cathedral, mixes solo organ works – including the great C minor Passacaglia and Fugue – with arrangements of pieces better known in their original guise. These include the cantata movement 'Sheep may safely graze', popularised by Myra Hess in her piano version, and Briggs's own arrangement of the best known of Bach's orchestral suites, containing the popular 'Air on the G String'. A number of the works in this early-evening organ recital receive the orchestral treatment in tonight's Bach Day climax (see *Prom 39*). *See 'Bach Bites', pages 68–69*

There will be no interval

SAME-DAY SAVER
Book for both Proms 38 and 39 and save (see page 155)

Broadcast
RADIO Live on Radio 3
ONLINE Live and 'listen again' options at bbc.co.uk/proms

Prom 39

Seats
£7 to £35

PRICE
BAND **A**

Prom 40

Seats
£7 to £35

PRICE
BAND **A**

7.30pm–c9.30pm

J. S. Bach, orch. Stokowski
Toccata and Fugue in D minor, BWV 565   *10'*

J. S. Bach, orch. Henry Wood
'Suite No. 6' – Prelude; Finale   *6'*

Tarik O'Regan
Latent Manifest   *c3'*
BBC commission: world premiere

Walton
The Wise Virgins – suite   *21'*

interval

Grainger
Blithe Bells   *4'*

J. S. Bach, arr. Sargent
Orchestral Suite No. 3 in D major,
BWV 1068 – Air   *6'*

Alissa Firsova
Bach Allegro   *c5'*
BBC commission: world premiere

J. S. Bach, orch. Bantock
Chorale Prelude 'Wachet auf, ruft uns die
Stimme', BWV 645   *5'*

J. S. Bach, orch. Respighi
Passacaglia and Fugue in C minor, BWV 582   *13'*

Royal Philharmonic Orchestra
Andrew Litton *conductor*

**SAME-
DAY SAVER**
Book for both
Proms 38 and 39
and save (see
page 155)

Andrew Litton

The grand finale to Bach Day features arrangements for orchestra made across almost a century. They range from the subtly coloured ballet score that William Walton drew from several of Bach's cantatas to the thunderous reinventions of organ works that begin and end the concert. Also appearing are Grainger's 'ramble' on 'Sheep may safely graze', Malcolm Sargent's recasting of 'Air on the G String', Granville Bantock's treatment of the popular chorale 'Sleepers, awake!' – and two special commissions from young composers who offer their new reimaginings based on movements from Bach's sonatas for solo violin and for viola da gamba. Having opened with the pure, pared-down period-performance approach stemming from the research of recent decades, Bach Day tonight lets its hair down in a glorious, if slightly unfashionable, celebration. *See 'New Music', pages 52–59; 'First Knight of the Proms', pages 62–65; 'Bach Bites', pages 68–69*

Broadcast
RADIO Live on Radio 3
ONLINE Live and 'listen again' options at bbc.co.uk/proms
TV Live on BBC Two

SUNDAY 15 AUGUST

Proms Plus Royal College of Music
1.00pm **Proms Family Orchestra and Chorus** Join us for a Russian-themed workshop. *See page 83 for details of how to sign up.*
4.45pm **Proms Literary Festival** James Meek, novelist and former *Guardian* Moscow correspondent, and Anthony Briggs, recent translator of *War and Peace*, discuss the great novelist Leo Tolstoy, 100 years after his death. Susan Hitch presents.
Edited version broadcast on Radio 3 during tonight's interval

6.30pm–c8.40pm

Musorgsky, arr. Rimsky-Korsakov
A Night on the Bare Mountain   *11'*

Shostakovich
Violin Concerto No. 1 in A minor   *38'*

interval

Scriabin
Rêverie   *4'*

Prokofiev
Symphony No. 3 in C minor   *35'*

Julia Fischer *violin*

London Philharmonic Orchestra
Vladimir Jurowski *conductor*

Vladimir Jurowski

Vladimir Jurowski and the LPO perform a dynamic, all-Russian programme. Julia Fischer returns to play Shostakovich's long-suppressed Violin Concerto, following her triumphant debut here two years ago – and she returns again even more swiftly to appear in tomorrow's Proms Chamber Music recital. Prokofiev's impassioned, sometimes spine-chilling Third Symphony originated in music from his opera *The Fiery Angel*. Musorgsky's feast of ghosts and ghouls appears in Rimsky-Korsakov's spectacular rearrangement, and we continue our Scriabin focus with the composer's fleeting dream-like rhapsody. *See 'Coloured Ambition', pages 46–49*

Broadcast
RADIO Live on Radio 3
ONLINE Live and 'listen again' options at bbc.co.uk/proms

MONDAY 16 AUGUST

1.00pm–c2.00pm

Proms Chamber Music at Cadogan Hall

Ysaÿe
Sonata No. 1 in G minor for solo violin   18'

Franck
Sonata in A major for violin and piano   28'

Julia Fischer *violin*
Milana Chernyavska *piano*

Julia Fischer   Milana Chernyavska

Following her Shostakovich concerto yesterday evening, Julia Fischer returns for the demanding and intensely expressive sonata by the Belgian virtuoso Eugène Ysaÿe. Her frequent chamber music partner, Ukrainian pianist Milana Chernyavska, joins her for the large-scale, Romantically turbulent sonata by César Franck, one of the works with which this late-flowering, Paris-based composer changed the course of French music.

There will be no interval

Broadcast
RADIO Live on Radio 3
ONLINE Live and 'listen again' options at bbc.co.uk/proms

MONDAY 16 AUGUST

Proms Plus 5.45pm, Royal College of Music
Proms Literary Festival Fifty years after the death of Nobel Prize-winning poet and author Boris Pasternak, Susan Hitch celebrates his work with Jonathan Myerson, who dramatised *Doctor Zhivago* for the BBC, and with professor of Russian, Donald Rayfield. With readings performed by Adjoa Andoh.
Edited version broadcast on Radio 3 during tonight's interval

7.30pm–c9.40pm

Scriabin
Symphony No. 1 in E major   50'

interval

Stravinsky
The Firebird   46'

Nadezhda Serdiuk *mezzo-soprano*
Sergei Skorokhodov *tenor*

London Symphony Chorus
London Symphony Orchestra
Valery Gergiev *conductor*

Valery Gergiev and the LSO perform Stravinsky's scintillating first ballet score for the Ballets Russes (composed 100 years ago), based on the Russian folk tale of the exotic Firebird imprisoned by the evil magician Kashchey. Scriabin was nothing if not ambitious: he began his symphonic output with a massive work in six movements, complete with a choral finale in praise of art and including two solo vocal roles, taken tonight by members of Gergiev's Mariinsky Theatre. *See 'Coloured Ambition', pages 46–49*

Nadezhda Serdiuk

Broadcast
RADIO Live on Radio 3
ONLINE Live and 'listen again' options at bbc.co.uk/proms

TUESDAY 17 AUGUST

Proms Plus 5.15pm, Royal College of Music
Composer Portrait Huw Watkins, in conversation with Andrew McGregor, discusses his new BBC commission and introduces his chamber works *Gig*, *Four Inventions* and *Sad Steps* (commissioned for the 2008 Proms Chamber Music series) – performed by the composer with musicians from the Royal College of Music.
Edited version broadcast on Radio 3 following tonight's Prom

7.00pm–c9.15pm

Arvo Pärt
Cantus in memoriam Benjamin Britten   7'

Britten
Four Sea Interludes from 'Peter Grimes'   17'

Huw Watkins
Violin Concerto   c20'
BBC commission: world premiere

interval

Shostakovich
Symphony No. 5 in D minor   50'

Alina Ibragimova *violin*

BBC Symphony Orchestra
Edward Gardner *conductor*

Having conducted Britten's *Peter Grimes* last year as Music Director of English National Opera, Edward Gardner joins the BBC Symphony Orchestra for the four evocative Sea Interludes from the opera. The heartrending strings and tolling bell of the *Cantus* by Arvo Pärt (75 this year) form a hypnotic tribute to Britten; and the programme ends with the Fifth Symphony by one of Britten's great friends – a work which brought Shostakovich back into favour with the Soviet authorities. Former Radio 3 New Generation Artist Alina Ibragimova performs the new concerto by Huw Watkins, who, as a pianist, often appears with her in recital. *See 'New Music', pages 52–59*

SAME-DAY SAVER Book for both Proms 42 and 43 and save (see page 155)

Broadcast
RADIO Live on Radio 3
ONLINE Live and 'listen again' options at bbc.co.uk/proms
TV Recorded for broadcast on BBC Four on 19 August at 7.30pm

TUESDAY 17 AUGUST

10.15pm–c11.30pm

Arvo Pärt
St John Passion   70'

Andrew Kennedy *Pilate*
Brindley Sherratt *Jesus*
Iain Farrington *organ*

Endymion
BBC Singers
David Hill *conductor*

David Hill

Estonian composer Arvo Pärt emerged on the landscape of late-20th-century music after making a decisive break from his former modernist ways and building a new language from scratch, using the simplest musical elements. The pure, hypnotic atmosphere of his slowly shifting harmonies has won him a place among the key figures of so-called 'spiritual minimalism', with a style that appears rooted in ancient religion while also sounding fresh and personal. Poised between the Lutheran and Catholic traditions, the austere yet serene *St John Passion* is sure to create a special aura in this ideal Late Night Prom setting.

SAME-DAY SAVER Book for both Proms 42 and 43 and save (see page 155)

There will be no interval

Broadcast
RADIO Live on Radio 3
ONLINE Live and 'listen again' options at bbc.co.uk/proms

WEDNESDAY 18 AUGUST

Proms Plus 5.30pm, Royal College of Music
Family Music Intro Bring your instrument and play along with musicians from the Russian National Orchestra, as Fraser Trainer leads you through music by tonight's composers.

7.30pm–c9.25pm

Beethoven
Overture 'Coriolan'   8'

Rachmaninov
Rhapsody on a Theme of Paganini   25'

interval

Tchaikovsky
Suite No. 3 in G major   38'

Nikolai Lugansky *piano*

Russian National Orchestra
Mikhail Pletnev *conductor*

Celebrating its 20th anniversary this year, the Russian National Orchestra returns to the Proms with its founder, Mikhail Pletnev, following a 14-year absence. After the drama of Beethoven's powerful overture to the play *Coriolan* (whose titular Roman general had inspired Shakespeare 200 years earlier), Nikolai Lugansky, one of today's renowned Rachmaninov players, takes the solo role in the variations of the

Mikhail Pletnev

'Paganini' Rhapsody – the first of a sequence of great pianists appearing at the Proms over the coming week. Tchaikovsky's Suite No. 3 – a form which the composer found more liberating than the conventions of the symphony – ends with another set of flamboyant variations.

Broadcast
RADIO Live on Radio 3
ONLINE Live and 'listen again' options at bbc.co.uk/proms

THURSDAY 19 AUGUST

Proms Plus 5.45pm, Royal College of Music
Composer Portrait James Dillon, in conversation with Andrew McGregor, discusses *La navette* (performed in tonight's Prom) and introduces his chamber works *Zone (… de azul)*, *Charm, dragonfly* and *… Once Upon a Time*, performed by Royal Scottish Academy MusicLab.
Edited version broadcast on Radio 3 following tonight's Prom

7.30pm–c10.20pm

Mozart
Der Schauspieldirektor – overture   4'

Liszt
Piano Concerto No. 1 in E flat major   19'

Rimsky-Korsakov
Sheherazade   45'

interval

James Dillon
La navette   20'
UK premiere

Tchaikovsky
Symphony No. 2 in
C minor, 'Little Russian'   35'

Boris Berezovsky *piano*

Boris Berezovsky

BBC Scottish Symphony Orchestra
Martyn Brabbins *conductor*

Marking the 75th anniversary of the BBC Scottish Symphony Orchestra, this packed concert recreates the night in 1962 when the orchestra first came to the Proms. A pair of Russian favourites is joined by Liszt's punchy First Concerto, in which Boris Berezovsky adds his name to the week's line-up of distinguished pianists. The only alteration to the original programme is that the new piece on that occasion – by Thea Musgrave (who has a commission later this season, see *Proms Saturday Matinee 5*) – is replaced with a premiere by another Scot, James Dillon (60 this year). See 'New Music', pages 52–59

Broadcast
RADIO Live on Radio 3
ONLINE Live and 'listen again' options at bbc.co.uk/proms

FRIDAY 20 AUGUST

> **Proms Plus** 5.15pm, Royal College of Music
> **Music Intro** Rachel Leach and members of the Philharmonia Orchestra give a jargon-free introduction to tonight's Prom. From a UK premiere to an old favourite in Ravel's Piano Concerto for the Left Hand, this introduction is designed to offer real insight to both first-timers and Proms regulars.

7.00pm–c9.00pm

Mosolov
The Foundry   4'

Arvo Pärt
Symphony No. 4, 'Los Angeles'   37'
UK premiere

interval

Ravel
Piano Concerto for the Left Hand   18'

Scriabin
The Poem of Ecstasy   20'

Jean-Efflam Bavouzet *piano*

Philharmonia Orchestra
Esa-Pekka Salonen *conductor*

The Philharmonia Orchestra and its Principal Conductor Esa-Pekka Salonen are joined by one of today's leading French pianists in Ravel's fiendish test of the left hand, stretching ears as much as fingers in a racy, sometimes macabre mix of styles from Romantic to jazz. In the climax to our 75th-birthday celebrations for Estonian Arvo Pärt, Salonen conducts the composer's first new symphony for over 35 years, having given the world premiere last year with the Los Angeles Philharmonic. Mosolov's clangorous outburst of 1920s industrial optimism, unheard at the Proms for 70 years, is complemented by Scriabin's breathtakingly prolonged crescendo of mystical sensuality. See *'Coloured Ambition', pages 46–49; 'New Music', pages 52–59*

Broadcast
RADIO Live on Radio 3
ONLINE Live and 'listen again' options at bbc.co.uk/proms
TV Broadcast on BBC Four at 7.30pm

FRIDAY 20 AUGUST

10.00pm–c11.20pm

Cage
First Construction (in Metal)   9'

Cardew
Bun No. 1   17'
London premiere

Howard Skempton
Lento   13'

Feldman
Piano and Orchestra   22'
London premiere

John Tilbury *piano*

BBC Scottish Symphony Orchestra
Ilan Volkov *conductor*

This late-night mixed platter of English and American Experimental traditions opens with John Cage's metallic *First Construction* – whose eight anvils and four car brake-drums resonate with Mosolov's *The Foundry* earlier this evening. Cornelius Cardew's *Bun No. 1* recalls a composer known as much for his political as for his musical activism. Howard Skempton, a co-founder with Cardew of the experimental Scratch Orchestra, and Morton Feldman, whose music Cardew championed in Europe, complete the line-up. See *'New Music', pages 52–59*

There will be no interval

SAME-DAY SAVER Book for both Proms 46 and 47 and save (see page 155)

Ilan Volkov

PROM 47
Spotlight on … John Tilbury

Though the American names of John Cage and Morton Feldman loom large in the field of Experimental music of the 1960s and 1970s, the movement also had its British heroes – notably, Cornelius Cardew and Howard Skempton.

'Cardew is neglected today in Britain, but his enormous importance is undisputed in many places around the world,' says pianist John Tilbury, who worked closely with the composer. 'His experiments with graphic notation, his music-making with amateurs and, more contentiously, his revolutionary political activism were very influential.

'Skempton's music creates space and release for both performer and listener, providing an antidote to the congestion that blights our lives. His pieces do not express a "form", but rather a state of being; in this he resembles Feldman.

'Most of Feldman's piano works are marked *ppp* – the aim is for the sounds to appear sourceless. The pianist's touch is therefore of the essence. As a pianist, you arrive at a venue and you rarely know what kind of instrument awaits you. So it's a truly experimental act! And with Feldman's beautiful and compelling sounds circulating in and around its nooks and crannies, the Royal Albert Hall is the perfect venue for his *Piano and Orchestra*.'

Broadcast
RADIO Live on Radio 3
ONLINE Live and 'listen again' options at bbc.co.uk/proms

SATURDAY 21 AUGUST

3.00pm–c4.30pm

Proms Saturday Matinee at Cadogan Hall

Dowland
Flow, my tears   5'

Britten
Lachrymae   15'

Gesualdo
Tenebrae Responsories for Maundy Thursday –
'Tristis est anima mea' (Responsory 2)   4'

Moro, lasso, al mio duolo   3'

Brett Dean
Carlo   21'

Monteverdi
Lamento della ninfa   6'

L'Orfeo – excerpts   13'

Betty Olivero
Neharot, Neharot   14'
UK premiere

Lawrence Power viola

I Fagiolini
Robert Hollingworth director
Britten Sinfonia
Ryan Wigglesworth conductor

Britten quoted Dowland's well-known lute song in his
Lachrymae, which spotlights the viola. Former Radio 3
New Generation Artist Lawrence Power also appears
in Israeli composer Betty Olivero's war-torn work that
draws on Monteverdi's *L'Orfeo*, as well as the laments
of mourning women. Brett Dean responds both to
Carlo Gesualdo's music and to his violent temper.
See 'New Music', pages 52–59

There will be no interval

WEEKEND PROMMING PASS • BEAT THE QUEUES AND SAVE MONEY (SEE PAGE 155)

SATURDAY 21 AUGUST

> **Proms Plus** 5.45pm, Royal College of Music
> **Proms Literary Festival** *Romanticism, Intuition and Emotion*
> Biographer and literary critic Jonathan Bate and playwright Gabriel
> Gbadamosi talk to Matthew Sweet about the shared themes of
> the Romantic movement, connecting its poetry, visual art and music.
> Edited version broadcast on Radio 3 during tonight's interval

7.30pm–c9.35pm

Wagner
Tannhäuser – overture   14'

Mahler
Rückert-Lieder   22'

interval

Beethoven
Symphony No. 3 in E flat major, 'Eroica'   50'

Simon Keenlyside baritone

Rotterdam Philharmonic Orchestra
Yannick Nézet-Séguin conductor

Yannick Nézet-Séguin

Making its first Proms
appearance with its new
young Music Director,
the Rotterdam
Philharmonic continues
the season's Wagner
series with the sweeping
overture to one of his
early epic dramas. They
are joined by one of
Britain's most sought-
after singers in Mahler's
affecting settings of Rückert poems on the subjects
of life, love and death. Initially dedicated to Napoleon
(until he declared himself Emperor), Beethoven's
'Eroica' Symphony made a lasting revolutionary
impact of its own, sustaining its heroic drama within
a new scale of dramatic expression. See 'A View of
Eternity', pages 24–31

PROM 48
Spotlight on … Simon Keenlyside

'Mahler's *Lieder* all have their own peculiarities:
the wittiness of *Des Knaben Wunderhorn*, the
grandiose quality of *Das Lied von der Erde*, the
perfect little jewel that is *Lieder eines fahrenden
Gesellen*, the inexpressible and unfixable despair
of *Kindertotenlieder*; and *Rückert-Lieder*, dealing
with the business of what it is to be a human
being and survive in the world.

'Ranging from the great swells of "Um
Mitternacht" (At midnight) to the most delicate
and fragile of thoughts in "Ich bin der Welt
abhanden gekommen" (I have become lost to the
world), the *Rückert-Lieder* really do require as
much colour and range as any singer can muster.

'There's something rather perfect about these
songs: the ecstacies of Mahler's seamless orchestral
lines; the tides of his dark sea of sound that
combines perfectly with the deep, shimmering
anxiety of the texts. They describe so wonderfully
how hard it is to live in the hurly-burly of this tail-
chasing world, and the unpredictable visitations
of joy and pain that come with that.

'At the end of 'Ich bin der Welt abhanden
gekommen', the decision to disengage oneself from
the world is not a sad one – not even, to my mind,
one made with resignation. It's an active choice,
made with strength and resolve.'

SUNDAY 22 AUGUST

Proms Plus 1.00pm, Royal College of Music
Proms Family Orchestra and Chorus Celebrate the
musicals of Rodgers and Hammerstein, in the 50th anniversary
of Hammerstein's death. *See page 83 for details of how to sign up.*

4.00pm–c5.30pm

A Celebration of Rodgers and Hammerstein

Cast to include:

Kim Criswell *vocalist*
Anna Jane Casey *vocalist*
Julian Ovenden *vocalist*
Rod Gilfry *baritone*

Maida Vale Singers
John Wilson Orchestra
John Wilson *conductor*

Following our Sondheim celebration in Prom 19,
Broadway lights up the Royal Albert Hall again to
honour the greatest creative partnership of American
musical theatre. It's 50 years since the death of Oscar
Hammerstein II, the lyricist whose partnership with
Richard Rodgers resulted in a series of inimitable hit
musicals. Returning with his orchestra of hand-picked
players, following their extraordinary debut at the
Proms last year, John Wilson conducts excerpts from
the movie orchestrations of *Carousel, Flower Drum
Song, Oklahoma!, The King and I* and *The Sound of
Music. See 'Bring on Broadway', pages 72–75*

There will be no interval

Rod Gilfry   Kim Criswell

PROM 49
Spotlight on ... John Wilson

'I've never had so many letters, emails and text
messages, and never over such a long period.'
Conductor John Wilson is recalling the warm
response to his Proms performance last year, in
which he revived lost scores of the MGM musicals.
'I can safely say that between the Prom and the
end of last year, not a single day went by without
a letter or an email about it. It shows there's an
enormous audience for this sort of concert if it's
done seriously.'

This year Wilson hopes to score a similar
success with his Rodgers and Hammerstein
celebration. 'The first thing I decided, given the
size of the Royal Albert Hall, was to use the
movie orchestrations. They're top-drawer
arrangements, supervised by both the composer
and lyricist, and sound better in the concert hall.
Also, to my knowledge, they've never been
performed in concert.'

Once again Wilson will bring his orchestra
of hand-picked dance-band and classical
musicians – a band put together with the
same care and devotion he holds for
Richard Rodgers. As he enthusiastically
confesses, 'I'm a real Rodgers nutcase.'

Broadcast
RADIO Live on Radio 3
ONLINE Live and 'listen again' options at bbc.co.uk/proms
TV Recorded for broadcast on BBC Two on 28 August

SUNDAY 22 AUGUST

Proms Plus 5.30pm, Royal College of Music
Family Music Intro Join Rachel Leach and musicians from
the BBC Symphony Orchestra in a family workshop designed
to uncover the secrets and delights of tonight's concert.
Bring an instrument and join in.

7.30pm–c9.30pm

Mozart The Magic Flute – overture	7'
Bartók Piano Concerto No. 3	25'
interval	
Bartók Cantata profana	19'
Haydn Symphony No. 102 in B flat major	25'

Richard Goode *piano*
Alan Oke *tenor*
Ashley Holland *baritone*

BBC Singers
BBC Symphony Chorus
BBC Symphony Orchestra
David Robertson *conductor*

The BBC Symphony Orchestra's Principal Guest
Conductor, David Robertson, makes the first of
two appearances this season. Between Mozart's
final operatic overture and the most determinedly
optimistic of Haydn's 'London' symphonies come
two contrasting works by Bartók: the unusually
mellow and good-humoured Piano Concerto No. 3,
featuring distinguished pianist Richard Goode,
and the compact burst of fierce vocal virtuosity
in which Bartók retells the Romanian
coming-of-age parable of nine young
hunters fleeing their roost.

SAME-DAY SAVER Book for both Proms 49 and 50 and save (see page 155)

Broadcast
RADIO Live on Radio 3
ONLINE Live and 'listen again' options at bbc.co.uk/proms

MONDAY 23 AUGUST

1.00pm–c2.00pm

Proms Chamber Music at Cadogan Hall

Song of Songs: sensuous polyphony from the courts of Renaissance Europe

Music by Ceballos, Clemens non Papa, Gombert, Guerrero, Lassus, Palestrina, Praetorius, Victoria and Vivanco, interspersed with plainchant

Stile Antico

Stile Antico

The Song of Songs, whose erotic imagery set the tone of the BBC Symphony Chorus's choral matinee (Prom 30), now lends its sensuality to a lunchtime immersion in Renaissance polyphony with the *Gramophone* Award-winning young British vocal ensemble Stile Antico. These conductorless singers have won praise for their performances and recordings of English Tudor and Elizabethan repertoire. This lunchtime's programme ranges from the clarity of Clemens non Papa to the rich textures of Victoria, and from the fervour of Gombert to the vigour of Praetorius.

There will be no interval

Broadcast
RADIO Live on Radio 3
ONLINE Live and 'listen again' options at bbc.co.uk/proms

MONDAY 23 AUGUST

Proms Plus 5.45pm, Royal College of Music
Proms Intro Conductor Thomas Dausgaard and composer Albert Schnelzer discuss tonight's programme with Martin Handley.

7.30pm–c9.40pm

Schumann
Symphony in G minor, 'Zwickau' (incomplete) 11'

Berlioz
Les nuits d'été 30'

interval

Albert Schnelzer
A Freak in Burbank 9'
UK premiere

Schumann
Symphony No. 2 in C major 38'

Nina Stemme *soprano*

Swedish Chamber Orchestra, Örebro
Thomas Dausgaard *conductor*

Eight years before he began his First Symphony in 1841, Schumann began an earlier one. Thomas Dausgaard – who has recorded a complete Schumann cycle with his agile Swedish Chamber Orchestra – opens with its sprightly first movement and ends our Schumann bicentenary symphony cycle
Nina Stemme

with the biggest and most stirring of the set. Swedish soprano Nina Stemme sings Berlioz's tender songs of love sought, found and lost, and her compatriot Albert Schnelzer pays tribute both to Haydn's playful character and to film director Tim Burton, born in the Californian city of Burbank. *See pages 34–37; 'New Music', pages 52–59*

Broadcast
RADIO Live on Radio 3
ONLINE Live and 'listen again' options at bbc.co.uk/proms

TUESDAY 24 AUGUST

Proms Plus 5.45pm, Royal College of Music
Proms Literary Festival Composer James MacMillan and religious poet Michael Symmons Roberts explore the strong relationship between poetry and the divine – as does Scriabin in his Symphony No. 3. Susan Hitch presents.
Edited version broadcast on Radio 3 during tonight's interval

7.30pm–c9.45pm

R. Strauss
Der Rosenkavalier – suite 22'

Ravel
Piano Concerto in G major 22'

interval

Scriabin
Symphony No. 3 in C major, 'The Divine Poem' 50'

Hélène Grimaud *piano*

Sydney Symphony
Vladimir Ashkenazy *conductor*

The Sydney Symphony returns to the Proms for the first time in 15 years, with its Music Director Vladimir Ashkenazy, a frequent guest here for more than 45 years. French-born pianist Hélène Grimaud, a Last Night soloist in 2008, plays the vivacious, blues-tinged concerto by Ravel. While the popular suite from Strauss's waltz-infused *Der Rosenkavalier* conjures up mid-18th-century Vienna, the intoxicating whirl of Scriabin's Symphony No. 3 relates to a cosmic dance between the human spirit and the universe.
See 'Coloured Ambition', pages 46–49

Hélène Grimaud   Vladimir Ashkenazy

Broadcast
RADIO Live on Radio 3
ONLINE Live and 'listen again' options at bbc.co.uk/proms

WEDNESDAY 25 AUGUST

7.30pm–c9.45pm

Mozart
Symphony No. 35 in D major, K385 'Haffner'   18'

Bent Sørensen
La mattina*   23'
UK premiere

interval

Grieg
Holberg Suite   20'

Mozart
Piano Concerto No. 24 in C minor, K491   31'

Leif Ove Andsnes *piano/director*

Norwegian Chamber Orchestra
Isabelle van Keulen *leader/director*
***Per Kristian Skalstad** conductor*

The Norwegian Chamber Orchestra visits with joint Artistic Director Isabelle van Keulen and Principal Guest Director Leif Ove Andsnes, taking charge from their respective instruments. Two contrasting works by Mozart – the sparkling 'Haffner' Symphony and the more dramatic C minor Piano Concerto – frame Scandinavian pieces new and old: Grieg's beloved string-orchestra classic and Danish Bent Sørensen's new piano concerto,

La mattina, which the composer regards as containing both his 'darkest and most profound' music.
See 'New Music', pages 52–59

Isabelle van Keulen

PROM 53
Spotlight on … Leif Ove Andsnes

Bent Sørensen's *La mattina* is the second work by the Danish composer to have been commissioned by Norwegian pianist Leif Ove Andsnes, following *Shadows of Silence*, which Andsnes premiered at Carnegie Hall in 1995.

'Sørensen had heard me perform Mozart concertos with the Norwegian Chamber Orchestra and liked the way we communicated,' says Andsnes. One of the concertos the composer heard was No. 17 in G major, K453, and for *La mattina* Sørensen adopted the same scoring of seven winds and strings.

'The piano writing is very dream-like,' explains Andsnes. 'The first movement is like a big sunrise, and, though there is some dark music, the whole piece feels like a journey towards light; it ends with a joyful dance.'

By contrast, Mozart's C minor Concerto, says Andsnes 'is more painful in its chromaticism than any of his other concertos, I think. For me, the last movement is the greatest set of variations he ever wrote. It is full of richness and variety, built on a compact and simple theme. Beethoven must have loved the work, as one can find many similarities with Beethoven's own Piano Concerto No. 3, also in C minor.'

THURSDAY 26 AUGUST

7.00pm–c9.00pm

Mark-Anthony Turnage
Hammered Out   c15'
BBC co-commission with Los Angeles Philharmonic: world premiere

Barber
Violin Concerto   25'

interval

Sibelius
Symphony No. 2 in D major   40'

Gil Shaham *violin*

BBC Symphony Orchestra
David Robertson *conductor*

David Robertson

In the second of his two Proms this season David Robertson conducts two enduring works by composers who fashioned a new aesthetic out of Romantic roots. The expansive melodies and edgy pace of centenary composer Samuel Barber are at their most powerful in the Violin Concerto, played here by Israeli-American virtuoso Gil Shaham. Sibelius's Second Symphony traces a path from terse drama to great affirmation. For his new commission in his 50th-birthday year, jazz-inspired Mark-Anthony Turnage has resolved not to write 'an old man's piece'. See 'New Music', pages 52–59

SAME-DAY SAVER Book for both Proms 54 and 55 and save (see page 155)

WEEKEND PROMMING PASS (SEE PAGE 155)

THURSDAY 26 AUGUST

10.15pm–c11.45pm

Jamie Cullum and the Heritage Orchestra

Jamie Cullum *piano/vocalist*
Heritage Orchestra

Singer and songwriter, pianist and guitarist, jazz leader and pop collaborator – Jamie Cullum has been doing it all for a decade. In a highlight of the Late Night Proms series he joins up with the Heritage Orchestra, the forward-looking, boundary-crossing collective formed six years ago to play at London's Cargo club. Soon they were recording a session for Gilles Peterson's Radio 1 show and appearing at the Montreux Jazz Festival. Cullum has devised a wide-ranging programme that also features new arrangements and some special guest appearances.

There will be no interval

Heritage Orchestra

PROM 55
Spotlight on … Jamie Cullum

Jazz crossover singer-songwriter Jamie Cullum is no stranger to large venues, but he's not blasé about returning to the Royal Albert Hall. 'The place carries a weight of expectation, a heaviness of all the music that's been played there in the past. You owe it to the venue to put on a good show. And the fact that you've played the big venues somehow doesn't stop you questioning your right to be there.'

For his Prom he'll be bringing the 40-piece Heritage Orchestra. 'They're one of our great young orchestras. They play with all sorts of musicians, from jazz and classical right through to Massive Attack, Unkle and Radiohead. We're developing a programme which takes in the full breadth of what I've done before.'

Though he's open to a range of influences, jazz stands at the core of Cullum's output. 'It's the linchpin of everything I do, but I grew up with pop, rock, hip hop and electronic music, so my tunes are brushed with all of that.

'I'm not from the kind of fluid school of piano playing you normally hear at the Proms,' says Cullum. Indeed, he feels, 'I fight with the piano on a daily basis, but I try to reach far beyond what I'm actually capable of. I think that brings a tension and energy to what I do.'

SAME-DAY SAVER
Book for both Proms 54 and 55 and save (see page 155)

Broadcast
RADIO Live on Radio 3
ONLINE Live and 'listen again' options at bbc.co.uk/proms
TV Recorded for broadcast on BBC Four on 27 August at 7.30pm

FRIDAY 27 AUGUST

Proms Plus 5.45pm, Royal College of Music
Proms Intro Brian Newhouse, host of the Minnesota Orchestra's broadcasts, and violist Sam Bergman discuss the works in tonight's Prom and orchestral life in Minnesota. Presented by Martin Handley.
Edited version broadcast on Radio 3 during tonight's interval

7.30pm–c9.50pm

Barber
Music for a Scene from Shelley   *7'*

Shostakovich
Cello Concerto No. 1 in E flat major   *29'*

interval

Bruckner
Symphony No. 4 in E flat major, 'Romantic'   *67'*

Alisa Weilerstein *cello*

Minnesota Orchestra
Osmo Vänskä *conductor*

Osmo Vänskä

Alisa Weilerstein

Osmo Vänskä, whose enthusiastic following in the UK dates from his tenure as Chief Conductor of the BBC Scottish Symphony Orchestra (1996–2002), returns for two Proms with the Minnesota Orchestra, which has seen a revival under his music directorship since 2003. Tonight the cinematic incidental music imagined by anniversary composer Samuel Barber for a scene from Shelley's *Prometheus Unbound* contrasts with the expansive splendour of Bruckner's 'Romantic' Symphony. Young American cellist Alisa Weilerstein makes her Proms debut in the first of Shostakovich's two concertos honed around the skill and stamina of the great Mstislav Rostropovich.

Broadcast
RADIO Live on Radio 3
ONLINE Live and 'listen again' options at bbc.co.uk/proms

SATURDAY 28 AUGUST

3.00pm–c4.30pm

Proms Saturday Matinee at Cadogan Hall

Robin Holloway
Fantasy-Pieces (on the Heine 'Liederkreis' of Schumann), Op. 16   28'

incorporating
Schumann
Liederkreis, Op. 24   21'

Schumann
Piano Quartet in E flat major, Op. 47   31'

Toby Spence *tenor*
Ian Brown *piano*

Nash Ensemble
Edward Gardner *conductor*

Our Schumann bicentenary survey continues with his amiable Piano Quartet, a work that occupies a similar place in artists' and audiences' affections to his Piano Quintet (see *Proms Chamber Music 2*). In the first of a trio of matinees that see today's composers respond to music of the past (see *Proms Saturday Matinees 5 & 6*), Robin Holloway, in his five *Fantasy-Pieces*, frames the Schumann song-cycle that inspired them. (His new take on another Schumann song-cycle features in Prom 74.) Edward Gardner conducts the Nash Ensemble in the second of his two Proms this year (see *Prom 42*). See *'A Mind Unhinged …?'*, pages 34–37

Edward Gardner

There will be no interval

Broadcast
RADIO Live on Radio 3
ONLINE Live and 'listen again' options at bbc.co.uk/proms

SATURDAY 28 AUGUST

Proms Plus 5.45pm, Royal College of Music
Proms Literary Festival *Schiller's 'Ode to Joy'* Singer-songwriter Billy Bragg, verse playwright Peter Oswald and poet David Constantine join Rana Mitter to discuss different interpretations of Friedrich Schiller's great work on unity and brotherhood.
Edited version broadcast on Radio 3 during tonight's interval

7.30pm–c9.40pm

Berg
Violin Concerto   28'

interval

Beethoven
Symphony No. 9 in D minor, 'Choral'   68'

Lisa Batiashvili *violin*
Helena Juntunen *soprano*
Charlotte Hellekant *mezzo-soprano*
Eric Cutler *tenor*
Neal Davies *bass*

BBC Symphony Chorus
Minnesota Orchestra
Osmo Vänskä *conductor*

Lisa Batiashvili

This year's performance of Beethoven's Ninth, a sought-after fixture of every Proms season, concludes the visit by Osmo Vänskä and the Minnesota Orchestra (see *Prom 56*), who together have recorded one of the most widely acclaimed Beethoven cycles of recent years. In the mystical heights and ecstatic momentum of the Ninth's final hymn to universal brotherhood they are joined by the BBC Symphony Chorus and a quartet of international soloists. Former Radio 3 New Generation Artist Lisa Batiashvili returns to the Proms to play the tragic and consoling violin concerto by one of the 20th century's most eloquent composers.

Broadcast
RADIO Live on Radio 3
ONLINE Live and 'listen again' options at bbc.co.uk/proms

SUNDAY 29 AUGUST

Proms Plus 4.45pm, Royal College of Music
Proms Literary Festival *Celebrating Czech Genius* How film-makers, cartoonists, puppet-makers and writers from Kafka to Václav Havel have skilfully depicted the surreal and absurd nature of modern life. Czech specialists Tim Beasley-Murray and Rajendra Chitnis join Rana Mitter.
Edited version broadcast on Radio 3 during tonight's interval

6.30pm–c9.20pm

Dvořák
Overture 'Carnival'   10'

Martinů
Fantaisies symphoniques (Symphony No. 6)   24'

interval

Grieg
Piano Concerto in A minor   30'

interval

Janáček
The Ballad of Blaník   8'

Dvořák
Symphony No. 8 in G major   35'

Lars Vogt *piano*

Czech Philharmonic Orchestra
Sir John Eliot Gardiner *conductor*

Famed over decades, the Czech Philharmonic returns to the Proms with a three-part celebration of music closely associated with it, including Dvořák's radiant Eighth Symphony, Martinů's equally colourful and spontaneous final symphony and a luminous musical legend by Janáček. Joining Sir John Eliot Gardiner, who makes the third of his four Proms appearances (see also *Proms Saturday Matinees 1 & 2 and Prom 75*), Lars Vogt offers a contrasting impression of musical nationalism in Grieg's intensely Norwegian and ever-fresh concerto – before returning to play more Janáček tomorrow lunchtime.

Broadcast
RADIO Live on Radio 3
ONLINE Live and 'listen again' options at bbc.co.uk/proms

MONDAY 30 AUGUST

11.00am–c12.30pm

Children's Prom

Programme to include:

Brahms
Hungarian Dance No. 5 in F sharp minor   *3'*

Lully
Alceste – two dances   *7'*

Prokofiev
Romeo and Juliet – Montagues and Capulets   *7'*

Rimsky-Korsakov
The Flight of the Bumblebee   *4'*

Satie, orch. Debussy
Gymnopédie No. 1   *3'*

and music by John Adams, J. S. Bach, Bernstein, G. Gabrieli and Shostakovich

Aurora Orchestra
Members of the National Children's Chamber Orchestra
Members of the National Youth Chamber Orchestra
Nicholas Collon *conductor*

Nicholas Collon

Boasting players aged as young as 10, the combined talents of the National Children's and National Youth Chamber Orchestras join the dynamic young professionals of the Aurora Orchestra to open our Bank Holiday Monday celebrations with a dazzling display of popular orchestral showpieces designed to introduce younger ears to the full splendours of the classical symphony orchestra (with a few surprises along the way!). See 'Deep Impact', pages 78–79

There will be one interval

Broadcast
RADIO Live on Radio 3
ONLINE Live and 'listen again' options at bbc.co.uk/proms

MONDAY 30 AUGUST

1.00pm–c2.00pm

Proms Chamber Music at Cadogan Hall

Janáček
In the Mists   *14'*

Schubert
Piano Sonata in G major, D894   *38'*

Lars Vogt *piano*

Lars Vogt

Following his performance of Grieg's Piano Concerto with the Czech Philharmonic Orchestra last night (Prom 58), German-born virtuoso Lars Vogt returns to pay his own tribute to Czech music with Janáček's last major piano work – its 'mistiness' captured in evocative harmonies and constantly shifting perspectives. By contrast, D894 is one of Schubert's more expansive sonatas, in which the easy-going tone is typically invaded from time to time by anguished intrusions but reasserts itself in a playful conclusion.

There will be no interval

Broadcast
RADIO Live on Radio 3
ONLINE Live and 'listen again' options at bbc.co.uk/proms

MONDAY 30 AUGUST

Proms Plus Royal College of Music
1.30pm Proms Family Orchestra and Chorus The last of the season. See page 83 for details of how to sign up.
5.00pm Family Music Intro A family-friendly introduction to tonight's Prom.

7.00pm–c9.00pm

Walton
Spitfire Prelude and Fugue   *8'*

G. Butterworth
The Banks of Green Willow   *7'*

Arnold
Four Cornish Dances   *13'*

Graham Fitkin
PK*   *c10'*
BBC commission: world premiere

interval

Bernstein
West Side Story – Symphonic Dances   *22'*

Gershwin
Shall We Dance? – Promenade ('Walking the Dog')   *3'*

John Williams
Hook – Flight to Neverland   *4'*

Various
You Must Remember This: A Cinematic Sing-Along   *8'*

Warren, arr. Don Sebesky
42nd Street   *5'*

***BBC Proms Family Orchestra and Chorus**
***Graham Fitkin** *conductor*
***Lincoln Abbotts** *conductor*
BBC Concert Orchestra
Keith Lockhart *conductor*

An evening of English classics and US pizzazz.

Broadcast
RADIO Live on Radio 3
ONLINE Live and 'listen again' options at bbc.co.uk/proms

TUESDAY 31 AUGUST

7.00pm–c9.25pm

Humperdinck

Hänsel and Gretel 107'

(semi-staged; sung in German)

Glyndebourne Festival Opera

Alice Coote *Hänsel*
Lydia Teuscher *Gretel*
Irmgard Vilsmaier *Mother*
William Dazeley *Father*
Wolfgang Ablinger-Sperrhacke *Witch*
Tara Erraught *Sandman*
Ida Falk Winhead *Dew Fairy*

Glyndebourne Chorus
London Philharmonic Orchestra
Robin Ticciati *conductor*

Glyndebourne Festival Opera makes its annual Proms visit with Laurent Pelly's semi-staged production of Humperdinck's glorious confection combining a popular Brothers Grimm fairy tale with Wagnerian music-drama. Robin

Robin Ticciati

Ticciati, former Music Director of Glyndebourne on Tour and now Principal Conductor of the Scottish Chamber Orchestra, makes his Proms debut, leading a strong cast led by Alice Coote and Lydia Teuscher, while Austrian tenor Wolfgang Ablinger-Sperrhacke uproariously plays the wicked Witch in drag. See 'Arias and Graces', pages 18–21

There will be one interval

PROM 61
Spotlight on ... Alice Coote

Former Radio 3 New Generation Artist Alice Coote has built a reputation for trouser roles. Having appeared in the 2008 Proms as Nero in *The Coronation of Poppaea*, she turns her sights from a Roman emperor to a little lost boy. 'Hänsel is unlike any of the other trouser roles,' Coote says. 'He's more innocent, playful, honest and vulnerable. It's a bizarre experience, psychologically, to perform him because when I step into those shorts I find my childlike soul hasn't grown up at all. I am still essentially a child inside, and it's so powerful and liberating to feel that coming so naturally from within.'

Though the tussle between the innocent children and the wicked Witch lies at the centre of the drama, for Coote, the opera's most moving scene is given over to the Mother. 'She sings of poverty and the dark heartbreak of a mother unable to provide for her children. It is an amazingly powerful portrayal of aloneness.'

Uniting the Glyndebourne Festival Opera cast is the rising British conductor Robin Ticciati. 'Robin has such gravitas,' observes Coote, 'but he is also young enough to remember being a child!'

Broadcast
RADIO Live on Radio 3
ONLINE Live and 'listen again' options at bbc.co.uk/proms

WEDNESDAY 1 SEPTEMBER

7.30pm–c9.55pm

Hindemith

Symphony 'Mathis der Maler' 27'

Mahler

Lieder eines fahrenden Gesellen 17'

interval

Bruckner

Symphony No. 9 in D minor 65'

Christian Gerhaher *baritone*

Gustav Mahler Jugendorchester
Herbert Blomstedt *conductor*

Christian Gerhaher

The last of this season's youth orchestras was founded a quarter of a century ago by Claudio Abbado as the first to recruit from both Eastern and Western Europe. It now returns under Herbert Blomstedt, Conductor Laureate of the San Francisco Symphony, to play Bruckner's last, unfinished symphony, Mahler's youthful song-cycle – with star baritone Christian Gerhaher as the lovelorn wayfaring lad – and the vivid symphony that Hindemith shaped from his opera about artistic heroism. See 'A View of Eternity', pages 24–31

Broadcast
RADIO Live on Radio 3
ONLINE Live and 'listen again' options at bbc.co.uk/proms
TV Recorded for broadcast on BBC Four on 3 September at 7.30pm

THURSDAY 2 SEPTEMBER

Proms Plus 5.15pm, Royal College of Music
Proms Literary Festival *Poetry and Music* British poet and librettist David Harsent joins Ian McMillan, presenter of Radio 3's *The Verb*, to celebrate the best poetry written about music – including Shakespeare, T. S. Eliot and Emily Dickinson.
Edited version broadcast on Radio 3 during tonight's interval

7.00pm–c9.10pm

Rameau
Dardanus – suite   *18'*

Canteloube
Songs of the Auvergne – selection   *25'*

interval

Martin Matalon
Lignes de fuite   *18'*
UK premiere

Musorgsky, arr. Henry Wood
Pictures at an Exhibition   *30'*

Anna Caterina Antonacci *soprano*

BBC National Orchestra of Wales
François-Xavier Roth *conductor*

The BBC National Orchestra of Wales returns under its French-born Associate Guest Conductor, François-Xavier Roth, for an all-French first half, coupling Rameau's sparky, quintessentially Baroque opera suite with Canteloube's sumptuous arrangements of traditional folk songs. After the interval, visual art provides the link between the Paris-based Argentinian composer Martin Matalon's subtly shaded *Lignes de fuite* – named after a drawing technique – and the rarely heard, and typically flamboyant, arrangement of Musorgsky's musical picture gallery that Proms founder-conductor Henry Wood made a few years before the more familiar version by Ravel. See *'First Knight of the Proms', pages 62–65*

PROM 63
Spotlight on … Anna Caterina Antonacci

Italian soprano Anna Caterina Antonacci is in demand on the world's opera stages, not least as the fiery *femme fatale* of Bizet's *Carmen*. Here she performs her selection from the lushly orchestrated and once highly popular *Songs of the Auvergne*, which Joseph Canteloube published in five series between 1923 and 1954. Though beguiling, these pastoral folk songs from the Auvergne region of France have fallen into neglect in recent decades, perhaps owing to their rich vein of nostalgia.

'Fashions change,' comments Antonacci, 'and yet these songs remain very beautiful and evocative. They seem ancestral – they could have been sung by the shepherds of Ithaca, or could still be heard today in some forgotten valley of Sardinia. They remind me of the poetry of Leopardi, of wind-blown landscapes. Even the shepherd-boy in Puccini's *Tosca* sings a similar song, and the atmosphere of dawn is instantly recalled. I would like to convey the sense of temporal abstractness of the solitary shepherd listening to the echo of his voice in the valleys. Even the sound itself should remain abstract, neither male nor female. For years I have heard these songs referred to as a true musical marvel, and I feel fortunate to sing them at the Proms.'

Broadcast
RADIO Live on Radio 3
ONLINE Live and 'listen again' options at bbc.co.uk/proms
TV Broadcast on BBC Four at 7.30pm

THURSDAY 2 SEPTEMBER

10.00pm–c11.15pm

W. F. Bach
Sinfonia in D minor   *9'*

Arne
Symphony No. 4 in C minor   *14'*

Pergolesi
Stabat mater   *39'*

Elizabeth Watts *soprano*
Anna Stephany *mezzo-soprano*

Early Opera Company
Christian Curnyn *conductor*

Elizabeth Watts   Anna Stephany

The Early Opera Company and its founder-conductor celebrate the anniversaries of three composers, all born in 1710: J. S. Bach's sadly wayward eldest son, Wilhelm Friedemann (see *also Proms Chamber Music 4*); the tragically short-lived Giovanni Battista Pergolesi, whose touchingly lyrical meditation on the sufferings of Christ's mother at the foot of the Cross has been winning new audiences; and the London-born Thomas Arne, once the leading British composer of his day, now known largely for writing *Rule, Britannia!* (see *Prom 76*).

There will be no interval

SAME-DAY SAVER
Book for both Proms 63 and 64 and save (see page 155)

Broadcast
RADIO Live on Radio 3
ONLINE Live and 'listen again' options at bbc.co.uk/proms

FRIDAY 3 SEPTEMBER

Proms Plus 5.45pm, Royal College of Music
Proms Literary Festival Philip Kerr, best-selling author of the *Berlin Noir* trilogy, discusses writing inspired by the city of Berlin, including work by Christopher Isherwood, John le Carré and Thomas Mann. Anne McElvoy hosts.

Edited version broadcast on Radio 3 during tonight's interval

7.30pm–c9.30pm

Beethoven
Symphony No. 4 in B flat major   34'

interval

Mahler
Symphony No. 1 in D major   55'

Berliner Philharmoniker
Sir Simon Rattle *conductor*

In the first of his two Proms with the Berlin Philharmonic, Sir Simon Rattle couples Beethoven's punchy Fourth Symphony – a work packed with drama beneath its sunny surfaces – with Mahler's First, which recalls the youthful song-cycle heard in Prom 62 while tracing a characteristic Mahlerian scenario of hard-fought triumph over personal doubts and demons. See 'A View of Eternity', pages 24–31

Sir Simon Rattle

Broadcast
RADIO Live on Radio 3
ONLINE Live and 'listen again' options at bbc.co.uk/proms

SATURDAY 4 SEPTEMBER

3.00pm–c4.30pm

Proms Saturday Matinee at Cadogan Hall

Judith Weir
All the Ends of the Earth   11'

Thea Musgrave
Ithaca   c10'
BBC commission: world premiere

Bayan Northcott
Hymn to Cybele   12'

Brian Ferneyhough
Dum transisset I–IV   12'
London premiere

Taverner
Dum transisset   6'

Jonathan Harvey
Dum transisset sabbatum   4'

Taverner
Missa Gloria tibi Trinitas – In nomine Domini (Benedictus)   1'

Gabriel Jackson
In nomine Domini   12'
BBC commmission: world premiere

BBC Singers
Arditti Quartet
Endymion
David Hill *conductor*

Judith Weir responds to 13th-century Parisian master Pérotin, while Brian Ferneyhough is inspired by Renaissance composer Tye. For their part, Jonathan Harvey and Gabriel Jackson glance backwards to Tye's contemporary Taverner. Thea Musgrave evokes the homecoming of Odysseus and Bayan Northcott sets the Latin poet Catullus. See 'New Music', pages 52–59

There will be no interval

Broadcast
RADIO Live on Radio 3
ONLINE Live and 'listen again' options at bbc.co.uk/proms

SATURDAY 4 SEPTEMBER

Proms Plus 5.45pm, Royal College of Music
Proms Intro Actor and comedian John Bird joins Julian Johnson (Professor of Music, Royal Holloway, University of London) to discuss tonight's programme. Presented by Petroc Trelawny.

7.30pm–c9.40pm

Wagner
Parsifal – Prelude (Act 1)   13'

R. Strauss
Four Last Songs   22'

interval

Schoenberg
Five Orchestral Pieces, Op. 16   16'

Webern
Six Pieces for Orchestra, Op. 6   12'

Berg
Three Pieces for Orchestra, Op. 6   21'

Karita Mattila *soprano*

Berliner Philharmoniker
Sir Simon Rattle *conductor*

In the first half of their second Prom, Sir Simon Rattle and the Berlin Philharmonic pair late works by two of Germany's greatest late-Romantics – 'Richard the First' and 'Richard the Third', as the conductor Hans von Bülow rather wickedly called them (quipping that, after Wagner, there could be no 'Richard the Second'). After the interval come sensational sonic adventures by the three great musical pioneers of early-20th-century Vienna. Celebrated Finnish soprano Karita Mattila returns to the Proms as soloist in Strauss's opulently nostalgic reflections on life's last days.

Broadcast
RADIO Live on Radio 3
ONLINE Live and 'listen again' options at bbc.co.uk/proms
TV Broadcast on BBC Two at 9.00pm

SUNDAY 5 SEPTEMBER · HENRY WOOD DAY

2.30pm–c6.00pm

Last Night of the Proms 1910

Wagner
The Flying Dutchman – overture   11'

Beethoven
Rondino for wind octet   7'

Paganini, arr. Pitt
Moto perpetuo   5'

Musorgsky, orch. Henry Wood
The Peep-Show   13'

Bizet
L'Arlésienne – excerpts   20'

David Matthews/Vaughan Williams
Dark Pastoral – based on the surviving fragment
of the slow movement of Vaughan Williams's
Cello Concerto (1942)   c11'
BBC commission: world premiere

Dvořák
Rondo in G minor   8'

Beethoven
Overture 'Leonore' No. 3   13'

Thomas
Mignon – 'Connais-tu le pays?'   4'

Dvořák, orch. Henry Wood
Humoresque in G flat major, Op. 101 No. 7   4'

Wagner
Kaisermarsch   10'

interval

Wood
Fantasia on British Sea-Songs   18'

German
Merrie England – 'Who were the Yeomen
of England?'   4'

Forster
Mifanwy   3'

Elgar
Pomp and Circumstance March No. 4
in G major   5'

The National Anthem   2'

Jennifer Larmore *mezzo-soprano*
Sergei Leiferkus *baritone*
Steven Isserlis *cello*

BBC Concert Orchestra
Paul Daniel *conductor*

Henry Wood

To open our day-long tribute to Proms founder-conductor Henry Wood, we present his own Last Night programme from a century ago – so producing the first Proms season ever to feature two Last Nights. While this parade of short popular classics truly recalls Promenade concerts of another age, we also continue Wood's commitment to new works – what Wood called his 'novelties'. So one short cello piece from the original 1910 programme is this afternoon replaced by a brand-new work, based on a movement from the unfinished Cello Concerto by Vaughan Williams. See 'New Music', pages 52–59; 'First Knight of the Proms', pages 62–65

Broadcast
RADIO Live on Radio 3
ONLINE Live and 'listen again' options at bbc.co.uk/proms
TV Recorded for broadcast on BBC Four on 9 September
at 7.30pm

Proms Plus 6.30pm, Royal College
Proms Literary Festival *From 'Howar*
A view of the cultural landscape of 1910,
afternoon's 1910 recreation. Historian Juliet Gardiner, art critic
Jackie Wullschlager and writer Juliet Nicolson join Matthew Sweet.
Edited version broadcast on Radio 3 during tonight's interval

8.00pm–c10.20pm

Bliss
Birthday Fanfare for Sir Henry Wood   2'

Bax
London Pageant   10'

Howell
Lamia   12'

Rachmaninov
Piano Concerto No. 1 in F sharp minor
(1917 version)   27'

interval

Sibelius
Karelia Suite   17'

Parry
Symphonic Variations   13'

Tchaikovsky
Eugene Onegin – Waltz and Polonaise   12'

Steven Osborne *piano*

Ulster Orchestra
Paul Watkins *conductor*

To close our Henry Wood Day, the Ulster Orchestra and its Principal Guest Conductor Paul Watkins play music either premiered by or closely associated with the founder-conductor of the Proms, opening with the fanfare that Arthur Bliss, the BBC's then Director of Music, wrote for Wood's 75th (and last) birthday in 1944, the year of the Proms' Golden Jubilee.
See 'First Knight of the Proms', pages 62–65

Broadcast
RADIO Live on Radio 3
ONLINE Live and 'listen again' options at bbc.co.uk/proms

MONDAY 6 SEPTEMBER

1.00pm–c2.00pm

Proms Chamber Music at Cadogan Hall

Venice: from the streets to the palaces

Le Poème Harmonique
Vincent Dumestre *theorbo/Baroque guitar/director*

As a curtain-raiser to our 400th-anniversary performance of Monteverdi's *Vespers of 1610* (see *Prom 75*), the vibrant French ensemble Le Poème Harmonique conjures up the carnivalesque atmosphere of 17th-century Venice, where the streets and palaces provided a cultural melting pot for the popular and artistic styles of the day. Along with one of Monteverdi's most famous madrigals, the *Lamento della ninfa*, the programme includes rarely heard music by Francesco Manelli, the first composer to write operas for the paying public as opposed to the privileged court.

There will be no interval

Le Poème Harmonique

PROMS CHAMBER MUSIC 8
Spotlight on ... Vincent Dumestre

Part concert, part theatre, this performance from French Baroque group Le Poème Harmonique evokes the spirit of 17th-century Venice – 'a time of great artistic freedom when "serious" music and more popular forms began to mix,' says the group's director Vincent Dumestre. This new musical language is heard in works by the poet-composer-singer Francesco Manelli. 'The interest of Manelli's music lies in its variety,' explains Dumestre. 'It ranges from light carnival music, using popular material of the time, to opera. Manelli is the true founder of Venetian opera, although unfortunately none of his operas has survived to the present day.'

The group also performs several works by Monteverdi, the most important composer of the day, including his *Lamento della ninfa*, 'one of the most beautiful laments on the theme of abandonment written in the 17th century,' says Dumestre. 'The music of the time could illustrate all kinds of moods within a very short period, so our concert will cover the whole range of emotions, from meditation to wit and humour.'

The group's aims are simple: 'It's about finding the right type of expression while respecting authenticity.'

Broadcast
RADIO Live on Radio 3
ONLINE Live and 'listen again' options at bbc.co.uk/proms

MONDAY 6 SEPTEMBER

Proms Plus 5.15pm, Royal College of Music
Proms Intro Conductor Stéphane Denève and musicians from the Royal Scottish National Orchestra join Petroc Trelawny in conversation about the music in tonight's Prom.

7.00pm–c9.10pm

Berlioz
Overture 'Roman Carnival'   9'

Beethoven
Piano Concerto No. 5 in E flat major, Op. 73 'Emperor'   38'

interval

James MacMillan
The Sacrifice – Three Interludes   15'
London premiere

Respighi
Pines of Rome   23'

Paul Lewis *piano*

Royal Scottish National Orchestra
Stéphane Denève *conductor*

The Royal Scottish National Orchestra and its French-born Music Director, Stéphane Denève, join Paul Lewis as he rounds off his cycle of the five Beethoven piano concertos with the last and most proudly majestic of them all. Taking up this afternoon's Italian theme, they play spectacular orchestral showpieces by Berlioz and Respighi, inspired respectively by Rome's lively street life and its imperial past; while, cementing Celtic connections, they introduce a recent symphonic suite drawn from the Scottish composer James MacMillan's opera The Sacrifice, inspired by the medieval folk tales of The Mabinogion and premiered to great acclaim by Welsh National Opera in 2007. See 'The Spirit of Beethoven', pages 40–43; 'New Music', pages 52–59

SAME-DAY SAVER
Book for both Proms 69 and 70 and save (see page 155)

Broadcast
RADIO Live on Radio 3
ONLINE Live and 'listen again' options at bbc.co.uk/proms

MONDAY 6 SEPTEMBER

10.00pm–c11.30pm

Handel
Julius Caesar – 'Empio, dirò, tu sei'   4'

Vivaldi
La fida ninfa – 'Aure lievi, che spirate'   6'

Orlando furioso – 'Sol da te,
mio dolce amore'   5'

Orlando furioso – 'Sorge l'irato nembo'   4'

Telemann
Concerto in E minor for recorder,
flute and strings, TWV 52e1   15'

Porpora
Polifemo – 'Alto Giove'   5'

Vivaldi
Orlando furioso – 'Ah sleale …
Io ti getto elmo'   6'

Concerto in D major for two violins,
strings and continuo, RV 513   15'

La fida ninfa – 'Dimmi pastore'   3'

Marie-Nicole Lemieux contralto
Philippe Jaroussky counter-tenor
Laurence Paugam violin
Alexis Kossenko recorder
Jean-Marc Goujon flute

Ensemble Matheus
Jean-Christophe Spinosi director/violin

French counter-tenor Philippe Jaroussky and
Canadian contralto Marie-Nicole Lemieux sing
arias and duets by two great masters of 18th-
century *opera seria*, including a rare extract
from one of the works that Handel's
London rival Porpora wrote to show off
his star pupil, the legendary castrato Farinelli.

SAME-DAY SAVER
Book for both
Proms 69 and 70
and save (see
page 155)

There will be no interval

Broadcast
RADIO Live on Radio 3
ONLINE Live and 'listen again' options at bbc.co.uk/proms

TUESDAY 7 SEPTEMBER

Proms Plus 5.45pm, Royal College of Music
Music Intro Fraser Trainer brings to life tonight's groundbreaking
pieces by Debussy and Stravinsky, with the help of musicians from
the Orchestre National de France. Ideal for first-timers and those
who want to know more about these fascinating works.

7.30pm–c9.15pm

Debussy
Prélude à L'après-midi d'un faune   10'

La mer   24'

interval

Stravinsky
The Rite of Spring   33'

Orchestre National de France
Daniele Gatti conductor

In its first visit to the UK since Daniele Gatti became
Music Director, the Orchestre National de France
presents three great works linked to France and its
capital city. Dating from a decade before his
symphony of seascapes, *La mer*, Debussy's poetic
Prélude made its composer's name when it was
premiered in 1894, and created controversy when
Nijinsky danced his erotic choreography of it for
the Ballets Russes in 1912. A year later the Paris
premiere of Stravinsky's *The Rite of Spring* prompted
an even more sensational *succès de scandale* for
Diaghilev's company, causing the most famous riot
in musical history.

PROM 71
Spotlight on … Daniele Gatti

After a year of focusing on Mahler with the
Orchestre National de France, Italian conductor
Daniele Gatti is looking forward to leading the
group in a performance of music from the French
tradition of the early 20th century – 'a period
which I consider very rich,' he says.

Though the three pieces in tonight's Prom were
written within 20 years of each other, they contrast
widely in mood and atmosphere, representing 'very
important and different sides of a rich and creative
period. This programme shows the big differences
that developed during that time,' explains Gatti.

And it seems his French players have a natural
affinity for performing works from the era. 'The
orchestra has an extremely versatile sound and a
very natural approach to performing French music
from this period,' says Gatti. 'Their sound, in all
sections, is perfectly suited to reflect what is
required by this kind of music – that's why I'll
concentrate on bringing back the full range of
nuance that reveals the rich vein of creativity in
which these works were conceived.' Although Gatti
is a regular visitor to the Proms, this is his first
appearance here with the ONF – 'and I am very
glad that we are performing there together'.

Broadcast
RADIO Live on Radio 3
ONLINE Live and 'listen again' options at bbc.co.uk/proms

WEDNESDAY 8 SEPTEMBER

Proms Plus 5.15pm, Royal College of Music
Composer Portrait Tansy Davies, in conversation with Tom Service, discusses her new Proms commission and introduces her chamber works *grind show (electric)*, *salt box* and *neon*, performed by musicians from the Guildhall School of Music & Drama.
Edited version broadcast on Radio 3 following tonight's Prom

7.00pm–c9.00pm

Wagner
Lohengrin – Prelude (Act 3)   4'

Tansy Davies
Wild Card   20'
BBC commission: world premiere

interval

Bruckner
Symphony No. 7 in E major   61'

BBC Symphony Orchestra
Jiří Bělohlávek conductor

Bruckner, like his hero Wagner, composed on a vast scale. In his third Prom of the season, the BBC Symphony Orchestra's Chief Conductor, Jiří Bělohlávek, pairs the dashing festive prelude from Act 3 of Wagner's 'swan knight' romance with the most overarching and open-hearted of Bruckner's nine symphonies – a work whose slow movement was composed in the shadow of Wagner's death and enshrines Bruckner's musical memorial to the man he revered as the 'Master'. Always a composer of vivid and funky surprises, Tansy Davies promises in her new work to take us on a journey through the Tarot pack. See 'New Music', pages 52–59

SAME-DAY SAVER
Book for both Proms 72 and 73 and save (see page 155)

WEDNESDAY 8 SEPTEMBER

10.15pm–c11.30pm

Penguin Cafe
with special guest
Kathryn Tickell *Northumbrian smallpipes*

To end the season's Late Night series we celebrate a band of musicians popular for two generations. Penguin Cafe's quietly insidious blends of catchy material, sophisticated skill and slightly surreal unpredictability have long been familiar to listeners who may never have registered the names of performers or music. Originally dreamt up and fronted by Simon Jeffes until his death in 1997 – and also prompting David Bintley's successful ballet *'Still Life' at the Penguin Cafe* – the group's music has reappeared on the scene thanks to Jeffes's son Arthur, who has added new pieces to the menu. Joining them is star Northumbrian smallpiper Kathryn Tickell, a past guest of the original Penguin Cafe Orchestra.

There will be no interval

Kathryn Tickell

PROM 73
Spotlight on ... Penguin Cafe

Penguin Cafe is the latter-day reincarnation of the original Penguin Cafe Orchestra, founded in 1972 by Simon Jeffes, whose original music for the band music has always been notoriously difficult to describe. 'I think our recordings have been put in the classical, folk, pop, rock, avant-garde, chill-out, world and dance sections of record shops,' says Arthur Jeffes, the group's current leader (and son of Simon Jeffes). 'One description I like at the moment is that it's a kind of modern chamber folk – I like that it could apply to the music or the musicians.'

The band boasts an eclectic line-up of instruments, ranging from violin, cello and piano, to ukulele, dulcitone (a keyboard instrument whose hammers strike tuning forks), penny whistles and guitars. Kathryn Tickell, on Northumbrian smallpipes, joins the group for its first Proms appearance. 'I'm looking forward to playing with Kathryn very much,' says Jeffes. 'I've been a real fan for a long time. I find the expression she can get into the pipes sounds so effortless, and yet so clear and direct that I can't listen to her playing without smiling.'

For its Late Night Prom, the ensemble aims to offer 'a place where one can opt out of the dehumanising pressures of modern life and simply be. Without wanting to sound overly mystical about it, a space where the music can just simply exist.'

Broadcast
RADIO Live on Radio 3
ONLINE Live and 'listen again' options at bbc.co.uk/proms

146 **Booking opens 8.00am on 4 May**: online at bbc.co.uk/proms • by telephone 0845 401 5040* • in person at the Royal Albert Hall

THURSDAY 9 SEPTEMBER

Proms Plus 5.45pm, Royal College of Music
Proms Intro Proms Director Roger Wright looks back over the 2010 season with Petroc Trelawny and takes questions from the audience.

7.30pm–c9.40pm

Schubert
Symphony No. 8 in B minor, 'Unfinished'   *25'*

Schumann
Introduction and Allegro appassionato in G major, Op. 92   *16'*

interval

Robin Holloway
RELIQUARY: Scenes from the life of Mary, Queen of Scots, enclosing an instrumentation of **Schumann**'s 'Gedichte der Königin Maria Stuart'   *c16'*
BBC commission: world premiere

Mozart
Symphony No. 40 in G minor   *30'*

Dorothea Röschmann *soprano*
Finghin Collins *piano*

BBC Philharmonic
Gianandrea Noseda *conductor*

Dorothea Röschmann

To end our Schumann bicentenary survey, Irish pianist Finghin Collins plays the closest thing we have to a second Schumann piano concerto, while Robin Holloway offers a fresh slant on the composer's final song-cycle, which sets poems and prayers penned in exile and prison by Mary, Queen of Scots. Gianandrea Noseda and the BBC Philharmonic also include masterpieces by two other composers who sadly lived even shorter lives. See 'A Mind Unhinged …?', pages 34–37; 'New Music', pages 52–59

Broadcast
RADIO Live on Radio 3
ONLINE Live and 'listen again' options at bbc.co.uk/proms

FRIDAY 10 SEPTEMBER

Proms Plus 5.45pm, Royal College of Music
Proms Intro Sir John Eliot Gardiner discusses Monteverdi's *Vespers of 1610* with Donald Macleod.

7.30pm–c9.20pm

Monteverdi
Vespers of 1610   *95'*

Monteverdi Choir
London Oratory Junior Choir
Schola Cantorum of The Cardinal Vaughan Memorial School
English Baroque Soloists
His Majestys Sagbutts and Cornetts
Sir John Eliot Gardiner *conductor*

Four hundred years after Monteverdi published his great collection of church music, the assorted choral, vocal and orchestral splendours of what is now universally known as the *Vespers of 1610* bring this season's Venetian strand to its spectacular conclusion. With performers ranged around the Arena and Gallery as well as the main stage, Sir John Eliot Gardiner and his Monteverdi Choir return to the music with which they made their Proms debut in 1968, now joined by the expert period-instrumentalists of the English Baroque Soloists, and with the additional brass forces of His Majestys Sagbutts and Cornetts.

There will be no interval

PROM 75
Spotlight on … Sir John Eliot Gardiner

It was for a performance in 1964 of Monteverdi's *Vespers of 1610* that John Eliot Gardiner, then a 20-year-old Cambridge undergraduate, founded the Monteverdi Choir. Four years later he conducted the work's first complete Proms performance (in which the organist was Andrew Davis, future Chief Conductor of the BBC Symphony Orchestra). Gardiner has referred to the *Vespers* as 'the richest and most substantial single work of church music prior to the Bach Passions. To experience it either as a performer or as a listener is a major event, and there must be many who have been bowled over by the work on first hearing.'

Monteverdi produced this compendium of choral settings for liturgical use while in the service of the Gonzaga court in Mantua. Emerging as his first published collection of sacred music for almost 30 years, it has widely been seen as the calling card of a composer in search of a higher position. Some believe this melting pot of Renaissance polyphony and Baroque opulence to have been conceived for the galleries and balconies of St Mark's, Venice, where the composer became *maestro di cappella* in 1613. The space of the Royal Albert Hall offers its own potential for the separation of vocal groups, lending an impression of ritual and occasion.

Broadcast
RADIO Live on Radio 3
ONLINE Live and 'listen again' options at bbc.co.uk/proms
TV Live on BBC Four

SATURDAY 11 SEPTEMBER

Proms Plus 5.00pm, Royal College of Music
Proms Intro Start off your Last Night celebrations by joining vocal coach and broadcaster Mary King in a sing-along covering a variety of operatic treats.

7.30pm–c10.40pm

Last Night of the Proms 2010

Jonathan Dove
A Song of Joys   c5'
BBC commission: world premiere

Tchaikovsky
Capriccio italien   16'

Rococo Variations (arr. Rysanov)   19'

Parry
Blest Pair of Sirens   11'

R. Strauss
Verführung, Op. 33 No. 1
Freundliche Vision, Op. 48 No. 1
Ständchen, Op. 17 No. 2
Winterweihe, Op. 48 No. 4
Zueignung, Op. 10 No. 1   18'

interval

Chabrier
Joyeuse marche   4'

Smetana
Dalibor – 'Dobrá! Já mu je dám! … Jak je mi?'   3'

Dvořák
Rusalka – Song to the Moon   6'

Vaughan Williams
Suite for viola and small orchestra –
Prelude; Galop   6'

Wagner
Lohengrin – Bridal Chorus   5'

Rodgers and Hammerstein
Carousel – 'You'll never walk alone'   5'

Hans Zimmer
Pirates of the Caribbean:
Dead Man's Chest – Hornpipe   3'

Arne
Rule, Britannia!   8'

Parry, orch. Elgar
Jerusalem   2'

Elgar
Pomp and Circumstance March No. 1
in D major ('Land of Hope and Glory')   8'

The National Anthem   2'

Renée Fleming *soprano*
Maxim Rysanov *viola*

BBC Singers
BBC Symphony Chorus
BBC Symphony Orchestra
Jiří Bělohlávek *conductor*

Tradition meets high jinks as Jiří Bělohlávek conducts his second Last Night, while the spirit of Henry Wood presides, as always, over the grand finale of the Proms. Renée Fleming lends her lustrous soprano to music by Strauss, Dvořák and Smetana, former Radio 3 New Generation Artist Maxim Rysanov gives Tchaikovsky's popular cello variations a new voice, and loyal Prommers can spot the last traces of the season's Wood, Parry, Wagner, Rodgers and Hammerstein and opera themes. A festive new piece by Jonathan Dove opens the evening; a contemporary hornpipe forms an upbeat to anniversary composer Arne's *Rule, Britannia!*; and audiences around the UK can join the Royal Albert Hall crowd in singing along to excerpts from *Lohengrin* and *Carousel* in a climax to the BBC's opera season. See 'New Music', pages 52–59.

PROM 76
Spotlight on … Renée Fleming

'We should have a Proms festival in New York,' says American lyric soprano Renée Fleming. 'It's a wonderful way to popularise classical music and get young people interested. I remember my first Proms appearance in 2001: the audience, especially those standing in the Arena, were incredibly still and attentive; that was extraordinary.' This is Fleming's first Last Night and, having watched Last Night clips on YouTube, she believes she's prepared for the 'fun and craziness of it all'.

Fleming has long been associated with Strauss. 'He's my "home" composer in a way. Though I cover a range of repertoire, I almost don't sing a recital without including his songs. He's one of the great writers for the voice; his music is instantly recognisable and beautifully expressive. You can tell he loved the soprano voice.'

Given her Czech heritage (her great-grandparents were born in Prague), it's little wonder she has also won renown for the title-role of Dvořák's *Rusalka*, which she recently performed under Jiří Bělohlávek for the Metropolitan Opera, New York; or that former Czech President Václav Havel invited her to appear (also with Bělohlávek) at a concert last year in Prague to mark the 20th anniversary of the Velvet Revolution.

Broadcast
RADIO Live on Radio 3
ONLINE Live and 'listen again' options at bbc.co.uk/proms
TV First half live on BBC Two, second half live on BBC One

Booking opens 8.00am on 4 May: online at bbc.co.uk/proms • by telephone 0845 401 5040* • in person at the Royal Albert Hall

BBC Proms IN THE PARK

The Last Night magic, live in the open air!

BBC Proms in the Park is centred around a live concert with high-profile artists and presenters, culminating in a BBC Big Screen link-up to the Royal Albert Hall. So gather together your friends, pack a picnic and get ready for a fabulous night out. Further Proms in the Park concerts around the UK will be announced. Please check bbc.co.uk/promsinthepark for details.

If there isn't a Proms in the Park near to you, you can join the party via one of the BBC Big Screens around the country: Birmingham (Victoria Square), Bradford (Centenary Square), Bristol (Millennium Square), Cardiff (The Hayes), Derby (Market Place), Dover (Market Square), Edinburgh (Festival Square), Leeds (Millennium Square), Leicester (Humberstone Gate), Liverpool (Clayton Square), Manchester (Exchange Square), Middlesbrough (Centre Square), Norwich (Chapelfield Plain), Plymouth (Armada Way), Portsmouth (Guildhall Square), Swindon (Wharf Green), Waltham Forest (Walthamstow Town Square) and Woolwich (General Gordon Place). For more details of Proms relays on the Big Screens, visit bbc.co.uk/bigscreens.

Highlights of Proms in the Park will be included as part of the live coverage of the Last Night on BBC One and BBC Two, while digital TV viewers can choose to watch the Royal Albert Hall concert or Proms in the Park.

SATURDAY 11 SEPTEMBER, HYDE PARK, LONDON

Dame Kiri Te Kanawa *soprano*
José Carreras *tenor*

Royal Choral Society
BBC Concert Orchestra
Martin Yates *conductor*

with thanks to

THE ROYAL PARKS

Dame Kiri Te Kanawa

Join in the Last Night celebrations in Hyde Park with a host of internationally acclaimed musical stars, including Dame Kiri Te Kanawa and José Carreras, accompanied by Proms in the Park favourites the BBC Concert Orchestra, together with the winner of the BBC Radio 2 Kiri Prize — the station's nationwide hunt to find a new opera star.

The party gets under way with presenter Ken Bruce and artists including Björn Again.

For further details of all BBC Proms in the Park events, visit bbc.co.uk/promsinthepark.

Gates open 4.00pm; entertainment from 5.30pm

For details of how to order a picnic hamper for collection on the day, or to find out about VIP packages and corporate hospitality, visit bbc.co.uk/promsinthepark.

Tickets £30.00 (under-3s free) — now available
Online *via bbc.co.uk/promsinthepark*
By phone *from the Royal Albert Hall on 0845 401 5040* (a booking fee of 2% of the total value, plus £2.10 per ticket applies); from See Tickets on 0844 412 4630* (a transaction fee of £2.00, plus a booking fee of £1.25 per ticket applies)*
In person *at the Royal Albert Hall Box Office (Door 12, no transaction fee)*
By post *see page 151*

Special Offers
Friends and Family Group Ticket *Buy seven tickets and get the eighth ticket free. (Not available online/via the Proms Planner.)*
Early Bird Offer *Book by midnight on Friday 4 June and save £5.00 per ticket.*

Please note: *in the interest of safety, please do not bring glass items (including bottles), barbeques or flaming torches.*

*Calls cost up to 5p per minute (0844 numbers) and 4p per minute (0845 numbers) from a BT landline (plus a one-off connection charge of up to 8p). Charges from mobiles and other networks may be considerably higher.

Broadcast
RADIO Live on BBC Radio 2
ONLINE Live and 'listen again' options
TV Live via the red button on BBC Television

How to Book

This year sees the introduction of a simpler, faster and fairer booking system for the BBC Proms. **Tickets will go on sale online, by telephone and in person on Tuesday 4 May at 8.00am** and your ticket purchases will be confirmed immediately. Tickets may also be requested by post.

A booking fee of 2% of the total value plus £1.00 applies to all bookings, except those for Proms in the Park (see page 156) and those made in person at the Royal Albert Hall. Special arrangements apply for the Last Night of the Proms, owing to high demand for tickets (see page 153).

Please note: the previous two-stage Advance and General booking system, together with the postal booking form and old online request system, has been discontinued.

ONLINE BOOKING AND THE PROMS PLANNER

Book online at **bbc.co.uk/proms** from 8.00am on Tuesday 4 May. Full booking details are available on the website. In the case of exceptionally high demand, you may be held in an online waiting room: you will be informed how many people are in front of you in the queue.

Plan your Proms concert-going online at your leisure before tickets go on sale, at any time from 12 noon on Thursday 22 April until midnight on Monday 3 May. The new online Proms Planner (accessible via bbc.co.uk/proms) has been designed to make it easier and faster to buy Proms tickets. Once completed, your personal Proms Plan is ready for you to submit from 8.00am on Tuesday 4 May, making it as quick and easy as possible for you to purchase your tickets once booking opens. Owing to the expected high demand when booking opens, using the Proms Planner means that you may be more successful in securing your preferred tickets, as your booking is likely to be processed more quickly.

How to use the Proms Planner

- From 12 noon on Thursday 22 April select 'Plan your Proms tickets' at bbc.co.uk/proms. (You will be redirected to www.royalalberthall.com.)
- Select 'Create my Proms Plan', create an account and start choosing the concerts you would like to attend, along with the number of tickets and seating section. You can make changes to your Proms Plan at any time until midnight on Monday 3 May.

  Please note: this is a request system and there is no guarantee that the tickets you select in your Proms Plan prior to booking opening will be available once booking has opened.

- From 8.00am on Tuesday 4 May you must visit www.royalalberthall.com and log in to your Proms Plan. In the case of exceptionally high demand, you may be held in an online waiting room before you are able to log in: you will be informed how many people are in front of you in the queue. *You must submit your Proms Plan in order to make a booking.*

- Your Proms Plan will now have been updated to reflect live ticket availability and you will be given the chance to choose alternatives should your selected tickets have become unavailable.

- Confirm your online booking by submitting your Proms Plan and entering your payment details.

- You will be sent confirmation of your booking immediately by email.

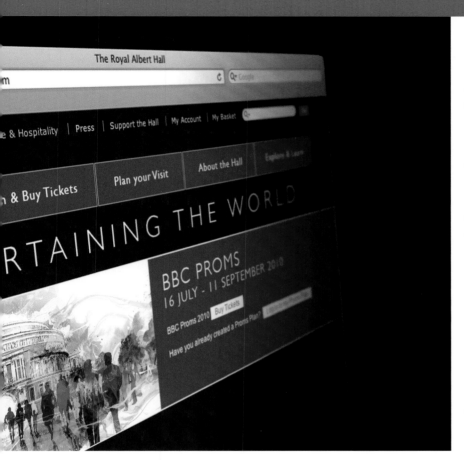

The Royal Albert Hall

BBC PROMS
16 JULY – 11 SEPTEMBER 2010
BBC Proms 2010 Buy Tickets
Have you already created a Proms Plan?

BOOKING BY TELEPHONE

From 8.00am on Tuesday 4 May, call the Royal Albert Hall Box Office on **0845 401 5040***. (The Box Office is open 9.00am–9.00pm daily and from 8.00am on 4 May.)

BOOKING IN PERSON

From 8.00am on Tuesday 4 May, visit the Royal Albert Hall Box Office at Door 12. (The Box Office is open 9.00am–9.00pm daily and from 8.00am on 4 May.) No booking fee applies to tickets bought in person.

BOOKING BY POST

The postal booking form has been discontinued. If you wish to apply for tickets by post, please write to BBC Proms, Box Office, Royal Albert Hall, London SW7 2AP with the following details:

- your name, address, telephone number(s) and email address (if applicable)
- the concerts you wish to attend
- number of tickets required
- preferred seating section, preferably with alternatives (see *seating plan on page 154 and ticket prices on page 156*)
- applicable discounts (see *pages 155 & 159*)
- a cheque made out for the maximum amount; or your credit card details, including type of card, name on the card, card number, issue number (Maestro only), start date, expiry date and security code (last three digits on back of Visa/Mastercard or last four digits on front of Amex).

Your details will be held securely. Postal bookings will be processed from 8.00am on Tuesday 4 May when booking opens.

TICKET TIPS

Don't give up!

If you are unable to get tickets for a popular Prom, **keep trying** at bbc.co.uk/proms or the Royal Albert Hall Box Office, as returns occasionally become available. In addition, many boxes and some seats at the Royal Albert Hall are privately owned, and these seats may be returned for general sale in the period leading up to the concert. The Royal Albert Hall does not operate a waiting list.

If you can't sit, stand

Up to 1,400 Promming (standing) places are available in the Arena and Gallery on the day for every Prom at the Royal Albert Hall. If you arrive early enough on the day of the concert, you have a very good chance of getting in. *For more details, see page 152.*

Why use the Proms Planner before booking opens?

- **Convenience** At any time from 12 noon on Thursday 22 April until midnight on Monday 3 May you can plan which Proms you would like to attend, and amend your selection.
- **Best chance for tickets** Creating your Proms Plan in advance speeds up the booking process and increases the likelihood of securing your preferred tickets when booking opens.

Please note: it is not possible to book entire boxes online. If you would like to book a full box, please call the Box Office on 0845 401 5040* from 8.00am on Tuesday 4 May.

If you have any queries about how to use the Proms Planner, call the Royal Albert Hall Box Office on **0845 401 5040***.

How to Prom

What is Promming?

The popular tradition of Promming is central to the unique and informal atmosphere of the BBC Proms at the Royal Albert Hall.

Up to 1,400 standing places are available for each Proms concert at the Royal Albert Hall. The traditionally low prices allow you to enjoy world-class performances for just £5.00 each (or even less with a Season Ticket or Weekend Promming Pass). There are two standing areas: the Arena, located directly in front of the stage, and the Gallery, running round the top of the Hall. All spaces are unreserved.

Day Prommers

Over 500 Arena and Gallery tickets (priced £5.00) go on sale two and a half hours before each performance (except Late Night Proms when tickets go on sale following the main evening performance; and 11.00am concerts when tickets go on sale at 9.45am). These tickets cannot be booked in advance, so even if all seats have been sold, you always have a good chance of getting in (though early queuing is advisable for the more popular concerts). You must buy your ticket in person, and must pay by cash.

Arena and Gallery tickets are available only at Door 11 (Arena) and Door 10 (Gallery), not at the Box Office.

Wheelchair-users who wish to Prom (Gallery only) should queue in the same way but will be redirected to Door 8 once their ticket is purchased. For further information for disabled concert-goers, see page 159.

If you are in doubt about where to go, Royal Albert Hall stewards will point you in the right direction.

Season Tickets

Frequent Prommers can save money by purchasing Arena or Gallery Season Tickets covering either the whole Proms season (including the Last Night) or only the first or second half (ie Proms 1–37 or Proms 38–75, excluding the Last Night).

Season Ticket-holders benefit from:
- guaranteed entrance (until 10 minutes before each concert)
- great savings – prices can work out at less than £2.25 per concert
- guaranteed entrance to the Last Night for Whole Season Ticket-holders and special access to a reserved allocation of Last Night tickets for Half Season Ticket-holders (see page opposite)

Please note: Season Ticket-holders arriving at the Hall less than 10 minutes before a concert are not guaranteed entry and may be asked to join the day queue.

Season Tickets are non-transferable and two passport-sized photographs must be provided before tickets can be issued. Season Tickets are not valid for concerts at Cadogan Hall.

For further details and prices of Season Tickets, see page 156. You can also buy Weekend Promming Passes (see page 155).

Proms at Cadogan Hall

For Cadogan Hall day seats, Proms Chamber Music Series Pass and booking information, see page 158.

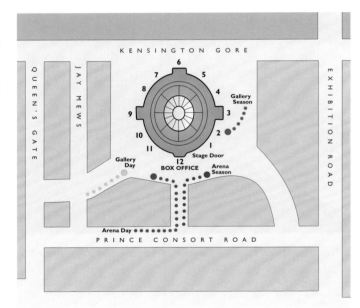

Where to Queue

- **Arena Day Queue**
  Enter by Door 11

- **Gallery Day Queue**
  Enter by Door 10

- **Arena Season Queue**
  Enter by Door 1

- **Gallery Season Queue**
  Enter by Door 2

The Last Night of the Proms

Owing to the huge demand for Last Night of the Proms tickets, special booking arrangements apply.

The majority of tickets for the Last Night of the Proms will be allocated by ballot to customers who have bought tickets to at least five other Proms concerts at the Royal Albert Hall. A further 200 tickets will be allocated by the Open Ballot (*see far right*).

The Five-Concert Ballot To be eligible to enter the Five-Concert Ballot, you must book tickets for at least five other concerts. You can apply to buy a maximum of two tickets for the Last Night. (Whether you book one or 11 tickets for five concerts, you will be offered a maximum of two tickets for the Last Night if successful in the Ballot.) If you are successful in the Ballot, you will not be obliged to buy Last Night tickets should your preferred seating section not be available.

Please note: you must also tick the Ballot opt-in box when booking online, or inform the Box Office that you wish to enter this Ballot when booking by telephone, in person or by post.

If you require a wheelchair space for Last Night of Proms you will still need to book for 5 other concerts but you need to phone the Access Information Line and request that you are entered into the separate ballot for wheelchair spaces by Monday 24 May. This ballot cannot be entered online.

Prom 67 (FREE Prom), concerts at Cadogan Hall and Proms in the Park do not count towards the Five-Concert Ballot.

The Five-Concert Ballot closes on Monday 24 May and you will be informed by Monday 31 May whether or not you have been successful. We regret that, if you are unsuccessful in the Five-Concert Ballot, no refunds for other tickets purchased will be payable.

General availability for the Last Night

Any tickets not allocated by the Five-Concert Ballot or the Open Ballot will go on sale on Friday 9 July. There is exceptionally high demand for Last Night tickets, but returns occasionally become available for sale, so it is always worth checking with the Box Office.

Please note: for all Last Night bookings, only one application (for a maximum of two tickets) can be made per household.

Promming at the Last Night

Day Prommers and Weekend Promming Pass-holders who have attended five or more other concerts (in either the Arena or the Gallery) can buy one ticket each for the Last Night (priced £5.00) on presentation of their used tickets (which will be retained) at the Box Office. A number of tickets will go on sale on Wednesday 21 July; a further allocation will be released on Wednesday 18 August; and a final, smaller allocation on Wednesday 1 September.

Season Ticket-holders Whole Season Tickets include admission to the Last Night. A limited allocation of Last Night tickets (priced £5.00) is also reserved for Half-Season Ticket-holders, and will be available to buy from the Box Office from Wednesday 21 July (for First Half Season-Ticket holders) and Wednesday 18 August (for both First and Second Half Season-Ticket holders). A final, smaller allocation available for both will go on sale on Wednesday 1 September.

Queuing Whole Season Ticket-holders and other Prommers with Last Night tickets are guaranteed entrance until 10 minutes before the concert. All Prommers (Day or Season) with Last Night tickets should queue on the South Steps, west side (Arena), or the top of Bremner Road, left side (Gallery).

Sleeping Out There has long been a tradition of Prommers with Last Night tickets sleeping out overnight to secure their preferred standing place inside the Hall. Official queues for ticket-holders will start at 4.00pm on the last Friday of the season. Those also attending Prom 75 will be given numbered slips to reserve their places in the queue, but must return immediately after the concert, and again in the morning. Please note, it is not necessary to camp out overnight.

On the Night Standing tickets are usually still available on the Last Night itself (priced £5.00, one per person). No previous ticket purchases are necessary. Just join the queue on the South Steps, east side (Arena), or the top of Bremner Road, right side (Gallery), during the afternoon and you may well be lucky.

Last Night of the Proms 2010 Open Ballot Form

One hundred Centre Stalls seats (priced £82.50 each) and 100 Front Circle seats (priced £55.00 each) for the Last Night of the Proms at the Royal Albert Hall will be allocated by Open Ballot. The Five-Concert Ballot rule does not apply, and no other ticket purchases are necessary. Only one application (for a maximum of two tickets) may be made per household.

If you would like to apply for tickets by Open Ballot, please complete the official Open Ballot form on the back of this slip and send it by post only – to arrive no later than Wednesday 30 June – to:

BBC Proms Open Ballot
Box Office
Royal Albert Hall
London SW7 2AP

Note that the Open Ballot application is completely separate from other Proms booking procedures. Envelopes should be clearly addressed to 'BBC Proms Open Ballot' and should contain only this official Open Ballot Form. The Open Ballot takes place on Thursday 1 July and successful applicants will be contacted by Thursday 8 July.

This form is also available to download from bbc.co.uk/proms; or call 020 7765 5407 to receive a copy by post.

Please note: if you are successful in the Five-Concert Ballot, you will not be eligible for Last Night tickets via the Open Ballot.

Last Night of the Proms 2010 Open Ballot Form

Title

Initial(s)

Surname

Address

Postcode

Country

Daytime tel.

Evening tel.

Mobile tel.

Email

Please indicate your preferred seating option‡

☐ I wish to apply for one Centre Stalls ticket (£82.50)

☐ I wish to apply for two Centre Stalls tickets (£165.00)

☐ I wish to apply for one Front Circle ticket (£55.00)

☐ I wish to apply for two Front Circle tickets (£110.00)

‡We cannot guarantee that you will be offered tickets in your preferred seating section. You will not be obliged to buy tickets outside your preference, but we regret we cannot offer alternatives.

The personal information given on this form will not be used for any purpose by the BBC or the Royal Albert Hall other than this ballot.

Choose Your Seat

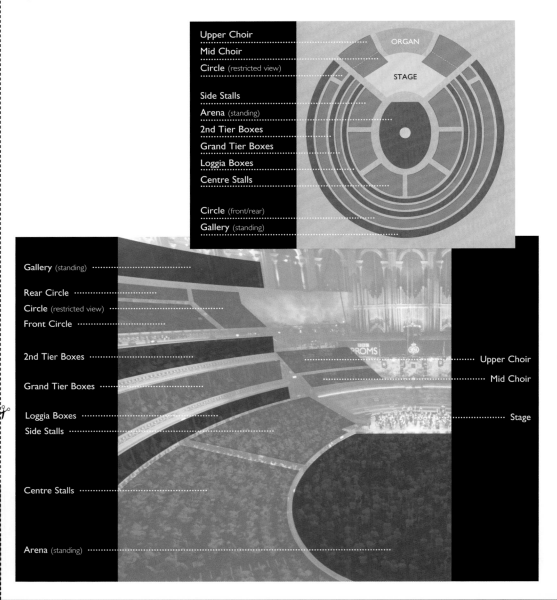

Upper Choir
Mid Choir
Circle (restricted view)
Side Stalls
Arena (standing)
2nd Tier Boxes
Grand Tier Boxes
Loggia Boxes
Centre Stalls
Circle (front/rear)
Gallery (standing)
ORGAN
STAGE

Gallery (standing)
Rear Circle
Circle (restricted view)
Front Circle
2nd Tier Boxes
Grand Tier Boxes
Loggia Boxes
Side Stalls
Centre Stalls
Arena (standing)
Upper Choir
Mid Choir
Stage

Special Offers

Same-Day Savers

Book seats for more than one concert on the same day, and save £4.00 per ticket for the later concert. This discount is available through all booking methods, including online and via the Proms Planner. When booking online it will be applied automatically at the checkout stage.

This offer applies to performances at the Royal Albert Hall only. Please note that Proms 59 (Children's Prom) and 67 (FREE Prom) are excluded from this offer, and it is not valid for Arena, Gallery and Circle (Restricted View) price bands. *See page 156 for price-band information.*

Kids Go Half-Price

The Proms are a great way to discover live music, and we encourage anyone over 5 years old to attend. Tickets for under-16s can be purchased at half price in any seating section for all Proms except the Last Night (Prom 76). This discount is available through all booking methods, including online and via the Proms Planner.

Note that the Doctor Who Proms on Saturday 24 and Sunday 25 July (Proms 10 & 11) and the Children's Prom on Monday 30 August (Prom 59) are expressly designed to introduce young children to concert-going.

Great Savings for Groups

Groups of 10 or more can claim a 10% discount (5% for C-band concerts) on the price of Centre/Side Stalls or Front/Rear Circle tickets (excluding the Last Night). *See page 156 for price-band information.*

Proms in the Park Make a real party of the Last Night in Hyde Park – buy seven tickets and get the eighth ticket free.

Please note: *group purchases can only be made by calling 020 7070 4408, or in person at the Royal Albert Hall. Group purchases cannot be made online.*

For more information, call the Group Booking Information Line on 020 7070 4408.

Proms in the Park Early Bird Offer

Book by midnight on Friday 4 June and save £5.00 per ticket (Hyde Park only).

Proms Chamber Music Series Pass

Attend all eight Proms Chamber Music concerts for just £30.00 with the Proms Chamber Music Series Pass (see page 158).

Weekend Promming Pass

Beat the queues at the weekend and save money! Promming is an essential part of the character of the BBC Proms. In addition to discounted tickets, the Weekend Promming Pass offers guaranteed access up to 10 minutes before start-time to the Arena or Gallery standing areas for all concerts in the Royal Albert Hall on Fridays, Saturdays and Sundays (excluding Proms 59, 75 and 76). Passes can be purchased online, by phone or in person at the Royal Albert Hall Box Office from 8.00am on Tuesday 4 May, and planned online via the Proms Planner from 12 noon on Thursday 22 April. Passes are available up to 6.00pm on the day they start (6.30pm on 16 July, 5.30pm on 6 & 20 August). Prices vary for each weekend depending on the number of concerts covered – see box below.

Note that Weekend 2 *excludes* Prom 11 (the second Doctor Who Prom), Weekend 7 (covering the August Bank Holiday) *includes* Prom 60, but *excludes* Prom 59 (Children's Prom). Weekend 8 *includes* Prom 67 (FREE Prom). There is no pass covering Proms 75 and 76. Weekend Promming Passes are not valid for concerts at Cadogan Hall.

Passes are non-transferable and signature ID may be requested upon entry. Purchase of a Weekend Promming Pass does not guarantee entry to the Last Night, but tickets may be counted towards the Five-Concert Ballot (see page 153) in conjunction with further Passes or Day Ticket stubs.

Please note: *you may purchase a maximum of four passes per weekend. Weekend Promming Passes are subject to availability.*

For Whole- and Half-Season Ticket prices, see page 156.

Weekend Promming Pass prices		
Weekend 1	Proms 1–3	£12.50
Weekend 2	Proms 9, 10 & 12	£12.50
Weekend 3	Proms 18–21	£17.50
Weekend 4	Proms 27–31	£22.50
Weekend 5	Proms 37–40	£17.50
Weekend 6	Proms 46–50	£22.50
Weekend 7	Proms 56–58 & 60	£17.50
Weekend 8	Proms 65–68	£12.50

Ticket Prices

Seats
Concerts fall into one of seven price bands, indicated above each concert listing on pages 110–147.

	A	B	C	D	E	F	G
Centre Stalls	£26.00	£36.00	£44.00	£15.00	£17.50	£82.50	
Side Stalls	£24.00	£32.00	£40.00	£15.00	£17.50	£80.00	
Grand Tier Boxes	£35.00	£44.00	£54.00	£15.00	£17.50	£90.00	
12 seats, price per seat	(As most Grand Tier Boxes are privately owned, availability is limited)						
Loggia Boxes 8 seats, price per seat	£30.00	£40.00	£48.00	£15.00	£17.50	£85.00	**ALL SEATS £12.00 (UNDER-16s £6.00)**
2nd Tier Boxes 5 seats, price per seat	£20.00	£25.00	£35.00	£15.00	£17.50	£72.50	
Mid Choir	£18.00	£21.00	£30.00	N/A	N/A	£60.00	
Upper Choir	£16.00	£19.00	£26.00	N/A	N/A	£55.00	
Front Circle	£14.00	£17.00	£22.00	£10.00	£14.00	£55.00	
Rear Circle	£11.00	£13.00	£17.00	£10.00	£14.00	£45.00	
Circle (restricted view)	£7.00	£8.00	£12.00	N/A	N/A	£25.00	

Promming
Standing places are available in the Arena and Gallery on the day for £5.00 (see page 152)

	Dates	Arena	Gallery
Season Tickets Whole Season (Proms 1–76)	16 July – 11 September	**£190.00**	**£170.00**
Half-Season Tickets First Half (Proms 1–37)	16 July – 13 August	**£110.00**	**£95.00**
Second Half (Proms 38–75)	14 August – 10 September	**£110.00**	**£95.00**

A booking fee of 2% of the total value plus £1.00 applies to all bookings, other than those made in person at the Royal Albert Hall.

Unwanted tickets may be exchanged for tickets to other Proms concerts (subject to availability). A fee of £1.00 per ticket will be charged for this service. Call the Royal Albert Hall Box Office (0845 401 5040*) for further details.

BBC Proms in the Park, Hyde Park, London, Saturday 11 September
All tickets £30.00 (Under 3's free) Details of this and other Proms in the Park events around the country, see page 149.
Friends and Family Group Ticket Buy seven tickets and get the eighth ticket free. (Not available online/via the Proms Planner.)
Early Bird Offer Book by midnight on Friday 4 June and save £5.00 per ticket.

Bookings for Proms in the Park tickets only will incur a booking fee of 2% of the total value plus £2.10 per ticket. No fee is payable if booking in person at the Royal Albert Hall.

Other Information

Disabled Concert-Goers
See page 159 for details of special discounts, access and facilities.

Privately Owned Seats
A high proportion of boxes, as well as 650 Stalls seats, are privately owned. Unless returned by owners, these seats are not usually available for sale.

Season Tickets
Season Tickets and Proms Chamber Music Series Passes can be booked online, by phone or in person at the Royal Albert Hall Box Office from 8.00am on Tuesday 4 May, and planned online via the Proms Planner from 12 noon on Thursday 22 April. Please note that two passport-sized photographs must be provided for each season ticket or pass before it can be issued.

Proms at Cadogan Hall
For booking information on the Proms Chamber Music series, see page 158.

Chris Christodoulou/BBC

Royal Albert Hall Kensington Gore, London SW7 2AP *(see map, page 160)* www.royalalberthall.com

Make the most of your visit and enjoy the full Royal Albert Hall experience. With 13 bars, three restaurants, box hospitality and a large array of products on offer, there is a wide range of food and drink for you to choose from.

Restaurants

Coda is a stylish restaurant offering an elegant dining experience with a modern British menu.

The **Elgar Room** offers a relaxed atmosphere ideal for any social gathering, be it cocktails while sharing a mezze platter or a three-course dinner with a bottle of wine.

Café Consort is fully licensed and offers a range of light meals and snacks. Post-concert food and drinks are also available on selected dates.

Further details will be sent with your tickets and will also be available from www.royalalberthall.com.

The **East Arena Foyer** serves a delicious selection of salads and desserts.

The restaurants open two hours before the performance, except the Café Consort, which opens two and a half hours beforehand. Tables should be booked in advance, except for the East Arena Foyer. Visit www.royalalberthall.com or call the Box Office on 0845 401 5040* to make your reservation.

Bars are located on all but the Gallery level, offering a full range of drinks, sandwiches, confectionery and ice cream. The East Arena Foyer, North Circle Bar, Moët & Chandon Champagne Bar and the porch bars at Doors 3 and 9 all open two hours before each concert. The porch bars at Doors 3 and 9 also offer coffee, sandwiches, salads and cakes. All other bars open 45 minutes before the start of the performance.

Interval orders can be arranged from any bar. Please ask any member of bar staff.

Box Hospitality

If you have seats in one of the Royal Albert Hall's boxes, you can pre-order catering. Please call 020 7589 5666 for details. Orders should then be confirmed in writing at least two working days before the concert that you are attending.

Please note: the consumption of your own food and drink in the Hall is not permitted. In the interests of health and safety, only cold soft drinks in closed plastic containers are allowed into the auditorium. Glasses and bottles are permitted in boxes, as part of box hospitality ordered through Leith's.

The relaxed atmosphere of the Elgar Room

Marcus Ginns

Car Parking

A limited number of parking spaces, priced £8.00 each, is available from 6.00pm (or one hour before weekend matinee concerts) in the Imperial College car park, which has entrances on Prince Consort Road (open Monday to Saturday until 7.00pm; closed on Sundays) and Exhibition Road. These can be booked online, by phone or in person at the Royal Albert Hall from 8.00am on Tuesday 4 May, and planned online via the Proms Planner from 12 noon on Thursday 22 April. Please note that, if attending both early-evening and late-night concerts, only one parking fee is payable.

Doors open 45 minutes before the start of each concert (earlier for restaurant and bar access) and 30 minutes before each late-night concert. This year, tickets will be scanned upon entry. Please have them ready, one per person.

Latecomers will not be admitted into the auditorium unless or until there is a suitable break in the music. There is a video screen in the Door 6 foyer with a digital audio relay.

Bags and coats may be left in the cloakrooms at Door 9 (ground level) and at basement level beneath Door 6. For reasons of safety and comfort, only small bags are permitted in the Arena.

Security

In the interests of safety, bags may be searched upon entry.

Children under 5

Out of consideration for both audience and artists, children under the age of 5 are not allowed in the auditorium.

Dress Code

Come as you are: there is no dress code at the Proms.

Mobile phones and other electronic devices are distracting to other audience members. Please ensure they are switched off.

The use of cameras, video cameras and recording equipment is strictly forbidden.

Tours of the Royal Albert Hall run every day and last approximately one hour. To book and to check availability, please call 020 7838 3105. Tickets cost £8.00 per person, with a number of concessions available.

The **Royal Albert Hall shop**, offering a selection of Proms and Royal Albert Hall gifts and souvenirs, is located inside the South Porch at Door 12. The shop is open daily from 10.00am until the start of the first performance each evening. Proms merchandise can also be purchased at the Door 6 foyer during performance times.

Cadogan Hall

5 Sloane Terrace, London SW1X 9DQ *(see map, page 160)* www.cadoganhall.com

Proms Chamber Music at Cadogan Hall

What better way to spend a summer Monday lunchtime than with an hour of chamber music? And when you're sitting in the light and airy surroundings of Cadogan Hall, the pleasure is sure to be enhanced. Proms Chamber Music returns for its 15th season with a variety of programmes reflecting Proms artists, anniversaries and special focuses. Mark Padmore and Imogen Cooper include a 200th-anniversary tribute to Schumann in their launch to the series, and Radio 3 New Generation Artists Meta4 and Francesco Piemontesi continue the theme with his Piano Quintet. Two more New Generation Artists, Malin Christensson and Henk Neven, delve into the riches of Wolf's *Italienisches Liederbuch*, and Proms debut artists Stile Antico explore an enticing programme of choral works from the Renaissance, based on the biblical Song of Songs. Julia Fischer and Lars Vogt, who both play concertos this season (see Proms 40 and 58), are featured in solo recitals, and Bach Day (Saturday 14 August) is heralded with trio sonatas from the Amsterdam-based ensemble Musica ad Rhenum, who also celebrate the 300th anniversary of J. S. Bach's eccentric eldest son, Wilhelm Friedemann. The season ends in a burst of colour with the French ensemble La Poème Harmonique evoking the spirit of Venice at the time of Monteverdi, with popular music from the theatre and street-corner – a curtain-raiser to Monteverdi's *Vespers of 1610* (see Prom 75). It's carnival time at Proms Chamber Music!

All Proms Chamber Music concerts are broadcast live on BBC Radio 3 and will be repeated the following Saturday at 2.00pm (except PCM 4, broadcast on Saturday 14 August at 2.45pm).

Doors open at 12 noon; entrance to the auditorium will be from 12.30pm

Proms Saturday Matinees at Cadogan Hall

Proms Saturday Matinees return to Cadogan Hall with a series of five concerts: Sir John Eliot Gardiner and the English Baroque Soloists perform Bach's six Brandenburg Concertos across two concerts on Bach Day; I Fagiolini and the Britten Sinfonia contrast Renaissance and contemporary works; there's Schumann and Robin Holloway performed by the Nash Ensemble; and a programme featuring two BBC commissions with the BBC Singers and the Arditti Quartet.

Doors open one hour before start-time; entrance to the auditorium is from 30 minutes before start-time

Cadogan Hall Ticket Prices

Stalls: £12.00
Centre Gallery: £10.00
Day seats (Side Gallery): £5.00

Tickets can be bought online, or by phone or in person from the Royal Albert Hall from 8.00am on Tuesday 4 May (0845 401 5040*) and from Cadogan Hall from Tuesday 11 May (020 7730 4500).

Tickets can be bought on the day of the concert – from Cadogan Hall only – from 10.00am.

£5.00 Tickets on the Day

At least 150 Side Gallery (bench) seats will be available for just £5.00 each from 10.00am on the day of the concert. These tickets can only be bought at Cadogan Hall. They must be purchased in person and with cash only, and are limited to two tickets per transaction.

£30.00 Proms Chamber Music Series Pass

Hear all eight Proms Chamber Music concerts for just £30.00, with guaranteed entrance to the Side Gallery until 12.50pm (after which Proms Chamber Music Series Pass-holders may be asked to join the day queue).

Passes can be purchased from 8.00am on Tuesday 4 May online, by phone or in person at the Royal Albert Hall. Two passport-sized photographs must be provided.

Please note: Proms Chamber Music Series Passes cannot be purchased from Cadogan Hall.

Proms Chamber Music Series Passes are subject to availability.

Royal College of Music

Prince Consort Road, London SW7 2BS
(see map, page 160) www.rcm.ac.uk

Proms Plus

Proms Plus pre-concert events will be held in the Amaryllis Fleming Concert Hall at the Royal College of Music.

All Proms Plus events are free of charge and unticketed (seating is unreserved), with the exception of the First Night live *In Tune* event on Friday 16 July, where free tickets will be available from BBC Studio Audiences (bbc.co.uk/tickets or 0370 901 1227†). Places must be reserved in advance for all Proms Family Orchestra and Chorus events and for the morning Wagner sessions on 17 July (visit bbc.co.uk/proms or call 020 7765 0643).

Please note: all Proms Plus events are subject to capacity and we advise arriving early for the more popular events. Latecomers will be admitted but, as many of these events are being recorded for broadcast, you may have to wait until a suitable moment. The event stewards will guide you.

For Prommers who join the Royal Albert Hall queue before the Proms Plus event, make sure you take a numbered slip from one of the Royal Albert Hall stewards to secure your place back in the queue.

If you have special access requirements, see the Royal College of Music information opposite.

†*Standard geographic charges from landlines and mobiles apply and calls may be included in your telecom provider's call package.*

Access at the Proms

Tickets and Discounts for Disabled Concert-Goers

Disabled concert-goers (and one companion) receive a 50% discount on all ticket prices (except Arena and Gallery areas) for concerts at the Royal Albert Hall and Cadogan Hall. To claim this discount call the Access Information Line on 020 7838 3110 (from 8.00am on Tuesday 4 May) if booking by phone. Note that discounts for disabled concert-goers cannot be combined with other ticket offers. Tickets can also be purchased in person from 8.00am on Tuesday 4 May at the Royal Albert Hall. The Box Office is situated at Door 12 and has ramped access, an induction loop and drop-down counters. Ambulant disabled concert-goers can also book tickets online (from 8.00am on Tuesday 4 May), and use the online Proms Planner from 12 noon on Thursday 22 April. Please note that the 'select your own seat' facility will not be available to customers booking online at this time – customers will be offered 'best available' seats within the chosen section. Wheelchair spaces cannot be booked online or via the Proms Planner.

The BBC Proms: access for all

Royal Albert Hall

Full information on the facilities offered to disabled concert-goers (including car parking) is available online at www.royalalberthall.com. Information is also available through the Access Information Line on 020 7838 3110 (open 9.00am–9.00pm daily and from 8.00am on Tuesday 4 May).

The Royal Albert Hall has up to 20 spaces bookable for wheelchair-users and their companions. There are two end-of-aisle places in the Side Stalls and two in the Centre Stalls – these places are priced as such; front-row platform places either side of the stage are priced as Side Stalls seats; rear platform places are priced as Front Circle seats. Spaces in the Front Circle are priced as such.

Four additional wheelchair spaces are available in the Gallery for Promming. These cannot be pre-booked.

Passenger lifts at the Royal Albert Hall are located on the ground-floor corridor at Doors 1 and 8. The use of lifts is discouraged during performances.

Hard-of-Hearing and Visually Impaired Concert-Goers

The Royal Albert Hall has an infra-red system with a number of personal receivers for use with and without hearing aids. To make use of the service, collect a free receiver from the Door 6 Information Desk.

If you have a guide dog, the best place to sit in the Royal Albert Hall is in a box, where your dog may stay with you. If you are sitting elsewhere, stewards will be happy to look after your dog while you enjoy the concert. To organise this, please complete an online Accessibility Request at www.royalalberthall.com or phone the Access Information Line

on 020 7838 3110 in advance of your visit (open 9.00am–9.00pm daily and from 8.00am on Tuesday 4 May).

Prom 19 on Saturday 31 July will be the first ever signed Prom. Dr Paul Whittaker, Artistic Director of Music and the Deaf will guide you through the music of Stephen Sondheim. When booking your tickets via the Access Information Line (020 7838 3110) please request the designated seating areas with the best visibility of the signer.

BBC Proms Guide: Non-Print Versions

From Friday 23 April audio CD and Braille versions of this Guide will be available in two parts, 'Articles' and 'Concert Listings/Booking Information', priced £3.00 each. For more information and to order, call RNIB Customer Services on 0845 702 3153*.

Programme-Reading Service

Ask at the Door 6 Information Desk if you would like a steward to read your concert programme out to you.

Large-Print Programmes & Texts

Large-print concert programmes can be made available on the night (at the same price as the standard programme) if ordered not less than five working days in advance. Complimentary large-print texts and opera librettos (where applicable) can also be made available on the night if ordered in advance. To order any large-print programmes or texts, please call 020 7765 3246. They will be left for collection at the Door 6 Information Desk 45 minutes before the start of the concert.

BBC Radio 3 Commentary

Visually impaired patrons are welcome to use the free infra-red hearing facility (see previous column) to listen in to the broadcast commentary on BBC Radio 3.

Cadogan Hall

Cadogan Hall has a range of services to assist disabled customers, including provision for wheelchair-users in the Stalls. There are three wheelchair spaces available for advance booking and one space reserved for sale as a day ticket from 10.00am on the day of the concert. For further information, please call 020 7730 4500.

Royal College of Music

The Amaryllis Fleming Concert Hall at the Royal College of Music has six spaces for wheelchair-users. Step-free access is available from Prince Consort Road, located to the left of the main entrance. For further information, please call 020 7591 4314.

Getting there

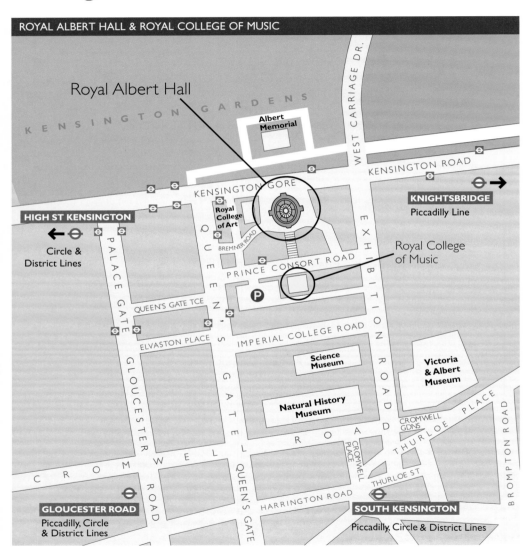

ROYAL ALBERT HALL & ROYAL COLLEGE OF MUSIC

The following buses serve the Royal Albert Hall and Royal College of Music (via Kensington Gore, Queen's Gate, Palace Gate and/or Prince Consort Road): 9/N9, 10/N10, 49, 52/N52, 70, 360 & 452. Coaches 701 and 702 also serve this area.

The following buses serve Cadogan Hall (via Sloane Street and/or Sloane Square): 11, 19, 22, 137, 170, 211, 319, 360, 452 & C1. For 24-hour London travel information, call 020 7222 1234 or visit www.tfl.gov.uk.

There are bicycle racks near Door 11 of the Royal Albert Hall. (Neither the Hall nor the BBC can accept responsibility for items lost or stolen from these racks.) The Royal Albert Hall has limited cloakroom space and may not be able to accept folding bicycles.

Please note: *all Proms venues lie inside the Congestion Charging Zone which operates 7.00am–6.00pm Mon–Fri.*

For car parking at the Royal Albert Hall, see page 157.

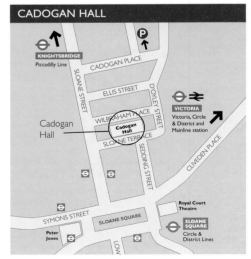

CADOGAN HALL

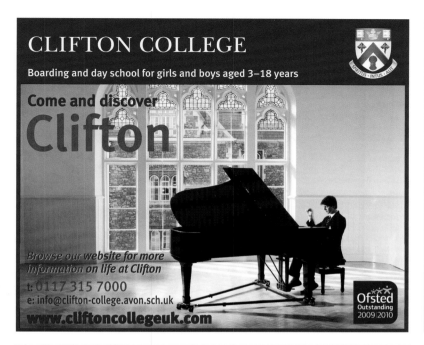
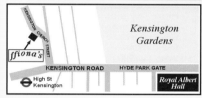
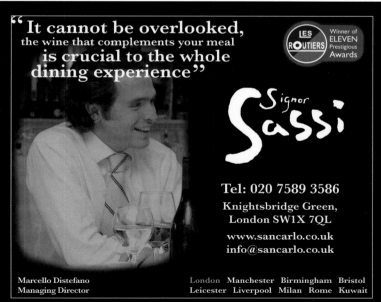

Index of Artists

Bold italic figures refer to Prom numbers
PCM indicates Proms Chamber Music concerts at Cadogan Hall
PSM indicates Proms Saturday Matinee concerts at Cadogan Hall
* first appearance at a BBC Henry Wood Promenade Concert
† current / ‡ former member of BBC Radio 3's New Generation Artists scheme

Index of Works

BBC Proms 2010
Director Roger Wright, Controller BBC Radio 3 and Director BBC Proms
Personal Assistant Yvette Pusey
Artistic Administrator Rosemary Gent
Concerts Administrator Helen Heslop
Radio 3 Events Co-ordinator Hélène Frisby
Concerts and Events Assistants Helen Lloyd, Catherine Langston,
Sarah Pantcheff
Head of Marketing, Publications and Learning Kate Finch
Publicist Victoria Bevan
Publicity Assistant Madeleine Castell
Marketing Co-ordinator Ellie Hoskin
Learning Manager Ellara Wakely
Learning and Audience Development Co-ordinator Naomi Selwyn
Management Assistant Tricia Twigg
Business Assistant Andrew Manning
Editor, BBC Radio 3 Edward Blakeman
Editor, TV Classical Music Oliver Macfarlane

BBC Proms Guide 2010
Editor Edward Bhesania
Sub-editor Clara Nissen
Publications Officer Lydia Casey
Design Premm Design Ltd, London
Cover illustration © Andy Potts
Publications Editor John Bryant
Published by BBC Proms Publications, Room 1045 Broadcasting House,
London W1A 1AA
Distributed by BBC Books, an imprint of Ebury Publishing, a Random
House Group Company, 20 Vauxhall Bridge Road, London SW1V 2SA
Advertising Cabbell Publishing Ltd, London (020 8971 8450)
Printed by Linney Print, part of the Linney Group, Mansfield. Linney Print
holds the ISO 14001 environmental management accreditation and has
FSC Chain of Custody Certification.
© BBC 2010. All details were correct at time of going to press.
ISBN 978-1-84607-978-8